Volume 1

The Academy of
Dental Management Consultants
Powerful Practice

Leading Consultants Share
Strategies for Dental Practice Success

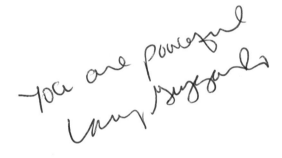

James &
Brookfield
J&B
Publishers

The Academy of Dental Management Consultants
Powerful Practice

Managing Editor: Gayle Smart
Book Designer: Paula Chance

Copyright ©2006

Disclaimer: This book is a compilation of ideas
from numerous experts who have each contributed a chapter.
As such, the views expressed in each chapter are those of the authors
and not necessarily the views of James & Brookfield Publishers.

For more information, contact:
James & Brookfield Publishers
P.O. Box 768024
Roswell, GA 30076

Library of Congress Catalog Number in Publication Data

ISBN: 0-9771912-6-5
Printed in the United States of America

10 9 8 7 6 5 4 3 2 1

Mission Statement: Our mission is to have a profound effect on the entire profession of dentistry by committing ourselves, as the ADMC, to excellence and professionalism through the establishment and maintenance of exceptionally high standards of practice. Those standards provide our members the opportunity of achieving extraordinary personal and professional growth. The Academy affords its members both a forum to exchange ideas and philosophies and the prestige of membership attained through the individual and collective realization of those exemplary standards.

Academy of Dental Management Consultants
P.O. Box 1270
Los Alamitos, CA 90720
(800) 451-9723 x 6061
Email: susand@trojanonline.com
Website: www.admc.net

W elcome to the first volume of *The Academy of Dental Management Consultants—Powerful Practice.* For years we have worked to use the collective talents of the Academy of Dental Management Consulting to help established and new dentists improve their practices. The goal of ADMC has been to share the best ideas in dental practice management in hopes of improving the skills of it's membership and ultimately their clients, the over 130,000 practicing dentists and their staff throughout the U.S. and Canada.

We are pleased to introduce to you the first of many editions of *The Academy of Dental Management Consultants—Powerful Practice.* As the current president of the ADMC I am pleased to present this edition to you and encourage you to give us your feedback in an effort to make the next edition of *The Academy of Dental Management Consultants— Powerful Practice* even more helpful to you and your colleagues. I particularly want to thank Linda Drevenstedt, a long time member of the Academy, for her determination and diligence in making this book a reality. Thanks for supporting the Academy of Dental Management Consulting.

Tim Breiding
ADMC President 2004-2006

T his is truly a "Blue Ribbon Winner!" With dozens of member organizations, hundreds of important topics, and thousands of learning opportunities available to dentists every year, you are holding a carefully crafted, invaluable recipe for success in your hands. This book, with its collection of original concepts and fresh ideas from some of the best and brightest minds in dental consulting today, is the dental educational equivalent to a "Taste of the City" event where experienced restaurateurs contribute their very best dish for you to taste, consider, evaluate, and enjoy. Each is unique and important as it is a personal creation from the basic ingredients available to all of us.

The Academy of Dental Management Consultants, or ADMC, is an organization dedicated to the advancement of practice success for dentists, dental teams, and the patients they serve. Our membership of experienced coaches and consultants is as diverse as dentistry itself with a multitude of varying specialties and expertise within dentistry's educational community. Fourteen highly-credentialed members have contributed a chapter on a practice management issue that they felt would not only be valuable but critical to dental practice success in today's competitive and ever-changing environment. The result is a collaborative book jam-packed with insights and tools for success gleaned from years of combined consulting experience in dental practices across the country just like yours. It really is a tasty example of each contributing consultant's best work, without the check! Our hope is that you will leave this table of knowledge with a deep, full sense of satisfaction combined with a hunger for more.

As you sample the offerings on this educational menu, we hope you will savor the passion and spirit of service in which each idea is presented. The members of the ADMC respect and admire the work you do for your patients and team members as well as the challenges you face every day in your endeavor to provide that service. It is our earnest hope that you will find much within the pages of this book that will inspire, enlighten, and simplify your personal road to success. We ask that you remember you do not walk that road alone, and if ever on your journey you need assistance, guidance, or a new perspective, we hope you will consider the Academy a valuable resource for qualified and deeply committed professionals who have dedicated their professional lives to making dentistry a better place to work and live. You can always reach us for referrals and assistance at www.admc.net or by calling Susan DiGiambattista, our executive director, at (800) 451-9723, ext. 6061.

On behalf of the entire membership of ADMC, we wish you abundance, joy, and a deep feeling of significance as you practice the amazing art and business of dentistry. *Bon Appetite!*

Katherine Eitel
ADMC President 2006-2008

TABLE OF CONTENTS

SUCCESSFUL MARKETING:
Telling the Story of YOUR Dental Practice

by Tim Breiding

One of my most enduring images of dental practice marketing comes from an old episode of the *Our Gang* (sometimes called *Little Rascals*) comedy shorts. In it, one of the gang has to go to the dentist, whose storefront office is marked with a plywood cutout of a huge tooth hanging over the door. In those simpler times (the *Our Gang* series was produced from 1922 to 1944), that was pretty much all the marketing that "Painless," the dentist, needed. Some practices don't go much beyond that even in the 21st century. Practitioners know that they have to have a marketing plan of a least some sophistication if they are going to build the practices that they want, doing the dentistry they like.

Notice that I am talking about "marketing," not "advertising." Marketing goes way beyond advertising and includes every facet of your practice, from your letterhead and business cards to the look and feel of your lobby, to your name tags and smocks, to how your staff answers the telephone and, yes, even to the magazines on your end tables.

When thinking about your marketing effort, it helps to consider it in terms of "Internal Marketing" and "External Marketing."

Internal Marketing
- Practice identity
- Stationery
- Practice brochure
- New patient package
- Signage

- Name badges
- Forms, both clinical and financial
- Customer Service/Patient Satisfaction Surveys
- Message on hold
- In office promotional material
- Yellow Page listings or display ads
- Website

External marketing
- Media plan
- Direct mail
- Newspaper ads
- Magazines
- Radio
- Television
- Public relations
- Public seminars
- Specialty advertising

Once the "look" is established, it is important that you use it consistently. All office materials should have the new look applied. Put it on everything from prescription pads to name tags. If you have control over your office signage, it needs to be applied there as well. Many practices we have worked with have done an excellent job of incorporating the new look on the wall of their reception area. Raised lettering or the graphic image used in your logo can often be combined with indirect lighting to create a dramatic presentation in your reception area. It is not by chance that most large corporations go so far as to publish a separate publication outlining the allowed usage of their logos in their marketing efforts. The choice of colors, type alignment, typeface, and wording needs to remain consistent. Once chosen, be sure to use your new look consistently in all applications of your marketing materials. *The goal is to present a professional image reflecting the quality and consistent dental care that you offer.*

Your Marketing Needs to "Hit 'em Where They Are"

Baseball great "Wee" Willie Keeler once summed up his hitting success by saying he merely "hit 'em where they ain't," meaning he hit the ball where the fielders weren't. Marketing a dental practice is exactly the opposite: you have to "hit 'em where they are," meaning your marketing has to hit people who are most likely to go to a dentist. What motivates people to seek dental care? There are as many opinions on this as there are types of treatment. My take is this. *Pain* is the primary motivator for the purchase of dental care. That pain can be either *physical*: I can't eat properly, my gums are bleeding or sore; or it can be *emotional*: I hate the way my teeth look, I'm embarrassed by my smile. In either case, the formula for marketing to those patients goes down the same path. Promote the type of dentistry first and yourself second. The potential patient is looking for the solution to a problem lead with marketing that identifies that problem and offers a solution in reassuring terms. They can find out what a great person you are once they have elected to come in for a consult. A friend and colleague and a leading dental author and coach, Dr. Paul Homoly, puts it best when he says, *"The greatest leverage in conceptual advertising is promoting target dentistry outside your office. The best way to build the relationship is to promote yourself inside the office. Promote the dentistry outside, yourself inside. Many dentists make the mistake of doing the reverse: they promote themselves outside and their dentistry inside. When they promote their dentistry inside the office, they come across tooth-centered."*

How Does External Marketing Work?

First, get comfortable with the fact that external marketing—advertising—takes time. I like to look at external marketing for dental and break it into two categories. The target in the ad can either be " promise-based" or "product based."

Promise-based advertising

With promise-based marketing you are offering hope, often with a longer term of care and a longer learning curve for the patient. You are offering a life-changing solution that can be higher in cost and requires excellent case presentation skills on the part of the doctor. The nature of this type of treatment requires a longer learning curve for the patient. It is for that reason that the "reach and frequency" aspect of advertising becomes so important. In advertising you have to reach a certain amount of targeted patients with a certain amount of frequency in order for the message to sink in. The frequency is usually about 3-5 times. You will be tired of seeing and paying for your advertisements a lot sooner than you will start seeing results. Most dental practices stop running their ads long before they start seeing the desired results. To complicate matters, the message has to hit the potential patient's hot button and needs to be in the market at the right time. The key to attracting "promised-based" patients is your patience. *This process is best accomplished with the help of advertising and a marketing professional.*

Product-based advertising

Product-based marketing involves selling specific services or procedures. An example would be an in-office or in-home whitening program, a public seminar, or a reduced fee on a specific type of dental care, such as an economy denture program. If the offer is worthwhile and your reputation is on par, the results for this type of marketing can be immediate. The only drawback to these types of offers is that the fee for the service is often reduced, and it makes cost-justifying the expenditure to market the product or service harder to live with. This type of marketing relies on a high volume of activity to support the effort. *Many clinics and large-volume practices have been successful with this tactic, but it isn't for everyone.*

Marketing Is Only a Tool, Not a Silver Bullet

There are several things that marketing can't do for you, and trying to shorten the process can only add to your financial and personal frustration. All the great marketing in the world can't put you in a market that matches your target and marketing goals. Do some research before you launch the effort. You can get a lot of free demographic and economic information about your market from the local media, the local chamber of commerce, or economic-development group. Selling high-level restorative dentistry in a depressed market can be done, but it takes all of the case-presentation skills you can muster and then some. You must have your clinical, management, and personal affairs in order. If your front desk turns over so fast that it looks like a turnstile, your problems are not going to be solved by marketing. In fact, successful marketing will compound the difficulty. It is also important that you have the clinical skills on the shelf that will allow you to deliver the level of care that you are promising. A weekend course in implants, sedation, and other high-level procedures is not enough.

It is music to my ears as a marketer when I ask a potential client where they received their training and I hear Pankey, Dawson, Spear, Misch, Homoly, Miles & Associates, Jameson, and a host of other highly qualified clinical and dental management firms. Go to market when you have

1. A target
2. A market survey
3. Clinical skills on the shelf
4. Financial stability
5. Qualified management and marketing consultants
6. A clearly defined marketing plan with goals, objectives, and accountability.

How Do I Get Started?

The most important element of successfully marketing your practice is a written plan. You can waste time and money if you don't have a plan to follow. Too many practices shoot from the hip when choosing which media they will use to attract new patients. Everything you do in the practice to market to prospective new patients and to existing patients needs to be scrutinized. In developing that plan, be sure to involve all of the team members who have a stake in the implementation and the outcome. If the practice is large enough, the doctor needs to appoint a team member to lead the plan. The elements of a plan tend to die in committee if there is not an ultimate decision maker at the helm. In any case, the doctor needs to stay involved with the process and be kept updated on the progress. If the process seems overwhelming, I would suggest hiring a qualified practice management consultant to facilitate the development of your plan. Be sure to pick a consultant who has marketing expertise.

Learn from others wherever possible. Don't limit your exploration to the dental community. Look at the trends in marketing in the major daily newspapers; subscribe to *Advertising Age*, read advertising and marketing books on targeting, positioning, creative strategies, and customer service. Local libraries are filled with a wealth of material on how to successfully market your services.

While there are similarities to dental practice operations both clinically and managerially, each dental practice has its own unique challenges and opportunities that shape the creation of an effective marketing plan. Be careful in buying "the package" or promotional programs that are off-the-shelf. Your materials need to be designed and implemented to fit the uniqueness of your practice. *No two practices are exactly alike. Have a written plan and things will happen.*

What Is The Best Way To Market?

Marketing touches nearly everything you do in your practice. If you are new to practice marketing, start off slowly and spend only what your current budget will permit without straining it. The only exception to this would be for a start-up practice. In that case, you should earmark a portion of the capital funds to support an initial launch and a modest ongoing campaign for the first year. Start by developing a list of all of the available and practical venues that can be used to create your plan. Break the list into two categories, placing actions or projects into either the internal or external category. There may be some gray areas in assigning to the lists; that is okay. It is important that the doctor and his or her team first establish a comfort level with marketing. If you are hesitant about a full blown, in-your-face marketing effort, just doing those items listed on the internal side of the plan will put you ahead of many of your competitors.

As the practice owner, you need to maintain the final say in all decision-making. It is important that you let those who will be ultimately responsible for the implementation of the plan have a say in the plan's development. *Establish a comfort level that suits you and your team and the nature of your market.*

Hold Yourself and Your Staff Accountable

Make sure that you have properly trained the staff with effective telephone skills. It is the first point of contact for your marketing efforts. An effective print ad or radio spot that attracts potential patients can be totally wasted through poor telephone techniques. There are several experts in the membership of ADMC that are available for training your staff. In addition to converting the call to the coveted office visit, it is also important to know the source of the referral. *When you are spending several thousand dollars per month marketing for new patients, you have to know what works and what doesn't.*

What Do I Want To Be?

Whether you elect to do internal marketing or external, or combinations of both, you have to develop a target market. I like to refer to it as choosing your 'threshold" for dental care. What type of dentistry would you rather perform than any other when you walk over the threshold each morning into your practice? What is your passion? For some it is complex implant cases. For others it is cosmetic procedures. It can also be becoming the best family dentist in your area. Whatever it is should become the lead in your marketing effort.

A word of caution, "Remember who brought you to the dance." No matter what your passion is, be sure to maintain a healthy base of the type of dentistry on which you have built your practice. Lead in your marketing with the type of dentistry that is your passion, but also mention that you are capable of doing basic or core dental procedures.

Most successful practices concentrating on cosmetic, implant, or other reconstructive dentistry have a solid base of general or family dentistry to fall back on. *Core dentistry can pay the bills while your passion can keep you sane and let you enjoy your work.*

And Now a Word About Branding

You are what you say you are. We often hear from practices that want to attract more complex dental cases. During our initial discussions, we find they are not fond of working with children, yet the practice name is something like "Family and Cosmetic Dentistry." Lead with your passion. Certain works will attract specific types of dentistry. If you want children, lead with the word family. Otherwise make it secondary or eliminate it all together. Be careful not to use dental jargon in your name. Words like "reconstructive" and "restorative" are more easily connected to a terrible auto accident than quality cosmetic dentistry.

Your logo or brand can reflect several images. The primary goal of the logo is to sell the type of dentistry you most want to perform. It can lead with your name, a geographic area, or other graphic or artistic images. The main point is that you keep the look professional, graphically pleasing, and, most importantly, on target. If your target is a high-level restorative dentistry, then cowardly lions, dancing extracted molars, and clinical instruments have no place in the design. The only exceptions to this are when you have a pediatric practice. You can have a little more fun in developing that look, but you also need to remember that parents, not the children, are making the choice of dental practices.

What Will Marketing Cost?

Many of the tasks in the internal side of your marketing are one-time costs. After the initial set-up, they may need future tweaking, but your ongoing cost should remain affordable and predictable. The larger your metropolitan market, the more expensive it will be for you to launch an effective campaign. Rural, small-town marketing costs are substantially lower than urban areas. These are broad statements since the fees associated with each market will be entirely different. Here are several analogies regarding the monthly costs associated with a campaign. Setting aside one-time costs, the monthly out-of-pocket costs for marketing in a large urban market may approach the cost of an average case fee for a full mouth restoration. In a rural market, a good analogy would be the income from an average cosmetic makeover. Your overhead, lab fees, and other local variables will affect the number of cases you need to attract on a monthly basis to justify the effort. In marketing for high-fee restorative dentistry, you need to look at the expenditure as a long-term investment for the future of the practice. Calls you receive today may not develop into accepted treatment for months and sometimes years down the road. Growth does not happen overnight; that is just whitening, remember.

You will make mistakes. If marketing were an exact science, most of us in the field would be out of business. You would simply buy the book, follow the instructions, and you'd be on your way to being the next Donald Trump of dentistry. A lot of good marketing ideas have grown from a lot more trial and error marketing. There really are no new ideas, just better and more creative approaches. Learn from others' mistakes and successes. Have fun in the process, don't be afraid to chalk mistakes up to experience, laugh often and move on the next challenge. *Marketing is not brain surgery and it can be a lot of fun. Good Luck!*

ABOUT TIM M. BREIDING

*W*ith over 19 years of dental marketing experience and 21 years with Knight-Ridder newspapers in marketing, advertising, and promotion positions, Tim brings a very versatile perspective to the process of dental practice marketing. He has helped hundreds of dental practices and dental consultants across the United States in developing effective marketing strategies. Tim is currently the President of the Academy of Dental Management Consultants (2005-2006). The roster of the ADMC represents many of the leading dental management consultants in the U.S. and Canada. Tim's style is informative and entertaining, taking the drudgery out of the marketing process.

Contact Information:
Tim M. Breiding
Breiding Marketing, LLC
11181 Scullers Run
Tega Cay, SC 29708
Phone: (803) 548-9868
Email: timtegacay@aol.com
Website: www.breidingmarketing.com

IF LIFE IS A FEAST, WHY AM I STARVING?

by Linda Drevenstedt, M.S.

Their practice is life for most dentists. Dentists and staff members, at various stages of their practice life, often share comments such as "Is this all there is?" "I am burned out." "If only I had a different staff." "If only I had a different boss." "If only I had better patients, all would be well." The reality is that there is a feast of opportunities out there that some dentists and staff members are enjoying, so why are you starving?

1. Don't Drink the Kool-Aid

The year was 1978. Jim Jones, a religious guru in Guyana, South America, asked his followers to consume a grape drink laced with cyanide. Over 900 men, women and children followed the directive and died. No one stopped to think for themselves about the request. Too often dentists and staff members become followers of another's dream of the ideal practice. There are many gurus in dentistry today. It seems there are new ones with every mail delivery. Dentists get caught up in what "THEY" say works or doesn't work. Consider another version of the Kool-Aid. Data, on *Star Trek*, was an android, a computer-generated being. Periodically, one of Data's computer chips would malfunction and his behavior would change. The chip had to be repaired or replaced so that Data could function at his highest level of efficiency.

We, too, have soft tissue chips that often malfunction and need repair or replacement. One of the damaged chips many of us carry around is the "They" chip. This chip in its malfunction can run your life and therefore ruin your practice. "They" are the tapes, voices, and good opinions of others in our lives that we carry in our head and in our heart. Often, dentists and staff proceed through life unaware of the influence of "They" on behavior, feelings, and thoughts about themselves and others. The "They" voice is programmed into our soft-tissue chip early in life. The scripts, expectations, and programming that "They" give us become a visceral integration into our being, often without our conscious knowledge. Much like a copy machine places no value on the items copied, our subconscious mind takes in impressions, feelings, stories, expectations, and programs from the "Theys" in our world. Often judgments about yourself and others are a product of "they" from our past. We drink the Kool-Aid that "They" gave us.

"They" tell you:

. . . you can't have that kind of practice in a small town, rural town, college town, blue collar area of the city.

. . . you will get the practice you want only if you do it "our" way.

. . . you can't find good help these days.

. . . you can't _____

. . . you should _____

Other "Theys" from our past might say you:

. . . need to do it perfectly or it and you are not OK.

. . . need to avoid conflict; just be nice to people; don't hurt their feelings.

. . . are married now; your life should be your family; don't get too ambitious.

. . . can't go back to school and finish that degree: you have children.

. . . are too young to do that; you are too old to do that.

. . . need to look at what you have; why do you want more?

. . . might lose what you have if you do that.

STOP—Don't drink anymore Kool-Aid. List the sources of "They" in your life. List the person and what "They" say. Now, put a plus for the positive "They"—there are a few. Then, put a minus beside the negative "They" voices in your life. Resolve to make your own way and ignore the negative "Theys" in your head. As soon as the "they" voice comes in, shoo it away with your own version of positive self-talk.

One young woman overcame her "They" by graduating from dental school and starting her own practice. Her husband left her with three small children. She could have stopped there, but she moved past the comments from her family. She finished college while living on welfare. Once she graduated, she was accepted into dental school and took out loans to support herself and her children. She is now the proud owner of her own dental practice.

2. "But I don't like spinach."

The feast of life often includes items we don't like. Even though Popeye got his strength from spinach, we often want the reward without tasting the spinach.

The "spinach" is the step you need to take to get out of that old familiar comfort zone. We hear comfort zone and think it does not apply to us. And yet, the quickest way to burn out in dentistry—or any profession for that matter—is to lull yourself into a comfort zone rut. Where, in your practice, are you avoiding discomfort?

Do you avoid talking to patients about the optimal heath your dentistry could provide for fear that they will reject your treatment plan? Comfort zones are subtle. One practice that I analyzed had a note in the chart beside certain teeth: "CIF." That was an unfamiliar notation so I asked the front office staff member. She said, "Oh, that means **C**rown **I**n **F**uture." The dentist would examine the patients, as I then observed, see a large amalgam, and tell the patent that the tooth would need a crown in the future. The dentist hated the "spinach" of telling the truth. "Mrs. Patient, the tooth has a large filling that has deteriorated and is beginning to crumble. To protect your tooth and prevent a possible broken tooth, I recommend a crown for your tooth." Because he avoided telling the truth, his day was interrupted with calls from patients with broken teeth. What do you avoid telling your patients?

What do you avoid telling your staff? Fear of losing the one you have and getting something worse, or no one at all, is a huge dish of "spinach" for many dentists. True leadership in the practice comes from telling your staff the truth about their performance and not expecting them to be mind readers.

In dentistry, we have poor new staff training, because dentists hire and put staff to work with little or no training. If there is a job description, that is a great first step. But having a training system is critical to the success of new staff. The training can take the form of a written training manual, or a home movie DVD of certain procedures or you can purchase, training DVD's or videos. There are many on the market if you search. Or you can ask a training mentor who is already in that position to train your staff. In the end, you have a responsibility to tell new staff members early and often what they are doing right and what needs to change or improve. When you start someone off with feedback, it becomes a part of your practice culture.

Champions become champions with coaching and feedback.

If you already have the staff but have avoided the "spinach" of feedback, go buy one can of spinach to place on your desk along with a box of tissues. One of the biggest reasons for avoidance is, "What if they cry?" So what if they cry? If you change your thinking to view crying or defensive communication as a ploy to get off the hook, then your dose of spinach will go down a lot better.

3. Don't Eat Dessert First

Dessert is sweet and goes down easy. Unfortunately, they don't sell EASY at Wal-Mart, (although there is an EASY button you can buy at Staples these days). The easiest way for you to miss a serving of your own potential in the feast out there is for you to wait, wish, and hope the other person will change and to think that you don't have to change. Right now, give up trying to change anyone. You can coach and give feedback to your staff, but, if the performance you need to have in your practice does not show up in 2-3 months, consider moving on. Fire this one and hire another one. Start the new one out with your feedback and training system in place.

Then look at yourself and see where you need to change to get to your vision. Do you need better emotional control? Do you snipe and throw temper tantrums? Do you give staff the silent treatment, expecting them to know why you are upset? Do you give, give, give to the staff or overlook behavior that needs to be addressed? Do you expect a magic bullet bonus system to solve your problems of motivation? Staff are "moved to action" (the meaning of the word motivation) with an inspired leader who has a vision that is compelling him/her forward. If you are in burnout or under-inspired, your influence creates a "ho-hum" soup of apathy in your practice.

Run, don't walk to a Leadership Course, not a clinical course, to revitalize your passion for dentistry and life. Too many dentists are clinically over-competent and under-competent in leadership. The EASY way is to take another clinical course. That's dessert.

4. Would you like some "whine" with your Cheese?

My son keeps a journal. One day he went back to some of his old journals and began to read. Lo and behold, he discovered he was writing the same old whines. For him this was a breakthrough moment when he took charge of the choices he was making in life. The moment you hear yourself whine to your spouse about the staff or the patients the moment you get home, whine to your office manager at the end of the day, whine to your colleague about something that is not working for you in your practice, STOP and address your whine.

Whines often come from two places.

1. Getting stuck in the rut of having the problem.
2. Having limitations that we hold onto for dear life.

Problem solving is a skill that can be learned. First, you go through the steps listed here. If the solution is not forthcoming, then the way out of the problem is to grow yourself through some limitation. There is an old saying that you cannot solve today's problems with yesterday's solutions. Yet, often dentists try to retrofit the solution.

Try this problem-solving recipe:

1. *Define the problem and the desired outcome.* This is not as easy as it looks. Japanese managers who have been whipping the competition in the US say to ask "Why" five times to get to the root cause of the problem. As you define the problem, ask "why?" does that happen.
2. *Collect data about the current situation.* What is the baseline of the problem? How often does it occur? Count and record your

data so that you have information to review. How does your data compare to any known benchmarks? This process may take a little research. Most problems in your practice are not new and have been solved by others who have tasted a different part of the feast out there.

Example: One dentist was obsessed with the problem of broken appointments. Once the count was in over a two-week period, his percentage was right at average. Looking at data helps keep the problem objective rather than emotional. It also makes us look at the reality of the outcome desired.

3. *Generate solutions.* This step needs a team of creative thinkers. Have everyone silently write solutions. Then break into small groups of 3 or 4 and share and discuss the listed solutions. Have the small group decide on the best No. 1 and No. 2 solution from the list.

4. *Choose the best solution in the larger group.* Weigh the pros and cons of the various suggested solutions. Evaluate time, staff and cost to implement the various solutions. Decide as a group which solution will be the chosen one. When your staff is a part of the solution, they have a vested interest in implementation and it works better.

5. *Implement the solution with all team members making a commitment to the solution.* Plan who and what each step will involve. As Nike says, Just Do It! Don't wait for the perfect time, the perfect person, the perfect anything—that is procrastination, which is pandemic in dental practices.

6. *Evaluate your solution within 60-90 days.* Make adjustments as needed.

If problem solving with your team does not solve your "Whine," it is time to get to work on you. Whines are crutches we use to avoid taking responsibility for our own change. Change is only welcomed by a wet baby, so the saying goes. It is fine for the other person but not for me. After all, I am the dentist, I have been working hard, I did have a rough time at home, I had abusive parents, I grew up in a broken home—as the kids today say, "Whatever" (must be said with attitude!). Change usually means facing a limitation that we fiercely hold onto. Change may even mean asking someone we trust to give us feedback about our behaviors that may be in the way of our success. Often we see ourselves as we intend to be, not as we really are. We see our world as we are, through our own "rose-colored" point of view, but we need to face some facts:

I may intend to be friendly to the patients, but in reality I may be chattering on *ad nauseum* about something that the patient cares little about.

I may intend to have high standards of quality, but the effect on people around me is that I never seem to be pleased with them.

I may intend to spare hurting your feelings, so I don't tell you the truth. The impact of my silence creates a judgmental barrier between us.

I may intend to create a cooperative team environment, but the effect might be never holding people accountable.

I may intend to push toward goals, but my impact might be that it seems to be only about the money.

If you have ever worked out with a trainer at the gym or a pro at another sport, you know the importance of feedback to get the moves correct for injury-free success. When a problem becomes a chronic whine, find a coach or a mentor to help reframe the behavior and to change in order to move into more of your potential.

Take some research time on "whines." Go home and ask your spouse to catalog them for a week. Ask your office manager or close colleague the same. Then, review your list and get to work on eliminating those whines. It may take finding a coach. It may take a weekend retreat on leadership or personal life transformation. Don't let the whines have their way with your mind. Face them square on and take responsibility for them. They are your own little demons to challenge and dissolve.

The saddest life is the unfulfilled one. As Thoreau said, "Most men live lives of quiet desperation." The saddest practice is one chugging along in a comfortable rut, running under potential. Dentistry is abundant with feasts at every corner. Don't get to the end of your practice days and look back at the feast left on the table while you were starving.

ABOUT LINDA DREVENSTEDT, M.S.

*A*s President of Drevenstedt Consulting, LLC, Linda has a wise and insightful process to assist dental practices in reaching their potential. Her "Steel Magnolia" approach shows you the way to Practice and Team Fitness™. Linda has been a practice management consultant for over 20 years. An expert in her field, she has been published in numerous professional journals including Journal of the American Dental Association, Dental Economics *and* Dental Practice Report. *She lectures at major conferences including the Hinman Dental Meeting, the American Dental Association, the Academy of General Dentistry, Denver Mid-Winter, and the Academy of Pediatric Dentistry. She holds undergraduate degrees in Dental Hygiene and Business Management, and an M.S. degree in Health Care Administration. In addition, she is a member of the National Speaker's Association, the Institute of Management Consultants, Academy of Dental Practice Administration, the Academy of Dental Management Consultants and a Board member of Enterprising Women in Leadership. Dentistry Today has voted her one of their "Leaders in Dental Consulting" for the past five years.*

Contact information:
Linda Drevenstedt
Drevenstedt Consulting, LLC
1093 A1A Beach Blvd., #378
St. Augustine, FL 32080
Phone: (800) 242-7648
Email: Linda@drevenstedt.com
Website: www.drevenstedt.com

HAVE THEM AT HELLO!™:
Thinking Differently About New Patient Phone Calls

by Katherine Eitel

There are two approaches to teaching advanced communication skills. One is to provide scripts: word-for-word dialogues to memorize and recite. The problem is that scripts never seem to work. Conversations rarely actually follow the script in real life. I'm not sure there's enough paper in the world to print out scripts for every possible variation of conversations you will likely encounter with patients. This approach really isn't logical and usually results in failure or, at the very least, non-compliance.

The second approach is to teach you to *think differently* about how you approach these calls and the common roadblocks to success. I find it much more empowering to give a dental administrator the conceptual tools necessary to handle any new patient call and any conflict about those calls that they might encounter. This approach allows the dental professional to remain more flexible, to stay focused on what the patient is trying to communicate (rather than on the next part of a script), and most importantly, to be authentic.

Some of you have a natural wit and sense of humor. Some possess a calm demeanor and are gracious and welcoming. Some are high-energy and enthusiastic. All of you are just as you should be: perfectly, uniquely you. My goal is to give you simple (not to be confused with easy) tools for improving your communications and, ultimately your results, with new patient phone calls and for allowing you to be the most authentic, genuine *you* that you can be.

There are four steps to a successful new patient phone call: Connection, Questions, Solutions, and Details. I will explain each of these in detail and give you examples of how I might approach each of them. Remember, the actual words you choose may be slightly different, depending on your personality and communication style. One thing I will always be (and can't communicate in this paper format) is friendly, upbeat, warm, and energetic—even when I don't necessarily feel that way. A true professional knows that is part of the job.

Whenever you try to improve any skill, it's important to start with the end in mind. In this case, the end you desire is to convert as many prospective callers to appointments as possible. You also want callers, whether they appoint or not, to hang up the telephone and feel amazed at how they were treated, listened to, and responded to. You want your team to exceed the caller's initial expectations. In addition, you want this goal obtained in an efficient amount of time and with consistency of message.

After reviewing nearly one hundred phone skills testing calls to dentists and other discretionary healthcare providers, I find that most employees use the computer screen or telephone intake slip to guide their call. This creates a very impersonal approach and is definitely not self-directed. Instead of using the computer screen to accomplish these objectives, consider the following four steps to transform your telephone calls from terrible to terrific:

Step One: CONNECTION

Make a quick but powerful personal connection with the patient. Let the caller know you are glad he or she called and get the person's name.

> *Office: "Thank you for calling Rancho Springs Dental. My name is Katherine. How may I help you?"*
>
> *Caller: "Hello. I was wondering if I could make an appointment to see the doctor?"*
>
> *Office: "Of course! I'm glad you called our office and I'd love to try to help you! Again, my name is Katherine. May I ask your name?"*
>
> *Caller: "My name is Carrie Simmons."*

Office: "*Great, Carrie! May I ask how you heard about us?*"

Caller: "*My neighbor, John Howard, told me about you and said that he was really happy with some cosmetic work that Dr. Roberts had done for him recently.*"

Office: "*Oh yes, Dr. Roberts does do beautiful cosmetic work. And we just love John. That was very kind of him to refer you to us. He always sends us the nicest patients!*"

Step Two: QUESTIONS

Once you've established rapport, get in the questioning seat as soon as possible. But be sure the questions you ask at this juncture are related only to discovering what the patient really wants and what the best solution to offer would be. These questions should not be about details such as social security number, address, or birth date. The appropriate time for those will come later.

Also, don't assume that the first question asked is the caller's true issue or real concern, or is the only thing for which he will schedule. Actually, my experience shows that it rarely is. People aren't just curious about which dentists in town take their insurance plan or the price dental crowns are going for these days. They have a dental problem and are looking for the dentist (hopefully on their plan but maybe not exclusively) that they feel good about to help them resolve it. Your objective is to uncover that problem and help them see why you are the best office to help them solve it. Even if their concern is prevention or their continued good health and they want to schedule a cleaning, the primary issue is not just who is a provider on their insurance plan.

The way to transition from Connection (Step One) to Questioning (Step Two) is with a statement such as: "*I want to give you the right information (appointment). Would you mind if I asked you a few questions first?*"

Office: "*Carrie, I want to be sure I give you the right appointment so would you mind if I asked you a few additional questions?*"

Caller: "*No, not at all.*"

Office: "*Great. Is there anything in particular, Carrie, that is bothering you or causing you any discomfort at this time?*"

Proceed with the patient, asking all the questions you need to clearly identify the real issues. Keep asking clarifying questions until you get that "Aha! I've got it!" understanding in your mind. Then you can offer a specific solution and sell your practice targeted toward the patient's needs, objectives, and concerns. You don't need to use every tool in your tool belt; you just need to identify the right tool and use that one skillfully.

Try to answer the caller's initial question with another question that helps you narrow the field of concerns to address. For example:

Caller: *"How much do you charge for crowns?"*

Office: *"Sam, I'd love to help you and I'm glad you called our office. I want to give you the right information so would you mind if I asked you a few questions first?"*

Caller: *"No."*

Office: *"Great, thanks. Why do you feel you need a crown at this time?"*

Another example:

Caller: *"Hi, my name is Beth Franks and I'd like to make an appointment to have my teeth cleaned, please."*

Office: *"Great, I'd be happy to help you and I'm so glad you've called our office, Beth. I want to make sure that I schedule the right appointment for you and the proper amount of time. Would you mind if I asked a few questions first?"*

Caller: *"No."*

Office: *"Great, thanks. Are you experiencing any discomfort or sensitivity at this time?"*

Your office may not agree philosophically with scheduling a cleaning before a comprehensive exam, but never start out by telling the patient, *"No, I'm sorry. We couldn't possibly know what kind of cleaning you will need, so you will have to have an examination with our doctor first to determine that."* This immediately puts you and the patient in an unnecessarily adversarial position. Much better to say, *"Yes, I'd be happy to schedule an appointment for you, but I want to be sure I schedule the right appointment and the correct amount of time, so would you mind if I asked you a few questions first?"* You can explore with the patient what kind of appointment (limited exam, comprehensive exam, complimentary cosmetic consultation, hygiene appointment, referral to another professional or specialist, or possibly sending more information) would be most appropriate given what you've learned about the patient's desires, needs, and concerns.

Step Three: SOLUTIONS

Offer the best solution based upon what you have discovered in the questioning phase. This becomes much easier to do once you've identified the patient's real concerns. The patient should never have to ask for an appointment. You must offer the appointment, or other solution, to the caller. Remember, once you identify the caller's main objectives and concerns, you have to sell your dentist and what your office has to offer specifically regarding those concerns. It's not up to the patient to sell themselves on you; it's up to you to sell them on you! However, don't take the shotgun approach to selling by spraying them with every good thing you've ever known about your doctor or your practice. Use the rifle approach by which you target your benefit statements directly to their individual concerns.

The transition statement to move from Questioning (Step Two) to Solutions (Step Three) would sound something like this:

"Beth, based on what you've just shared with me: you're having some mild sensitivity to cold on that lower left tooth. It's been a while since you've seen a dentist, and you want to stay healthy and prevent any future problems. I'd like to invite you in for a comprehensive examination with Dr. Connor."

"Let me tell you what that would include. Dr. Connor will take a comprehensive look at your teeth and gums, of course, paying particular attention to that lower left area that is sensitive. He will also assess the health of your jaw joint and your bite, as well as a screening for oral cancer. At that time, he will assess what type of hygiene appointment you would need and exactly how much time so we don't waste your time in any way. I think you will be very pleased with how thorough and complete Dr. Connor's exams are and how much he customizes his treatment recommen-

dations based on your concerns and objectives. Dr. Connor has an opportunity to see you for that appointment Wednesday at 3:00 or Thursday at 11:00. Which one fits your schedule best?"

It's important to build value for the solution to which you are steering the patient. You'll notice that the team member rolled right in to offering the appointment without stopping to ask if the patient wanted to schedule. Statistics show that most people go where you lead them if you lead them!

Step Four: DETAILS

Now, you can ask those detail questions that you have saved until after you've "made the sale." So many calls I listen to start out asking these questions before they know what the patient wants or even if the patient will schedule at all. It's very impersonal and does nothing to build a relationship or identify needs, not to mention that often we schedule the wrong kind of appointment for them based on what they originally asked for instead of one that will truly meet their needs. Additionally, it is always a good idea to end your call by reconfirming the appointment specifics as well as reassuring the patient what a good decision he or she has made. Here's a list to get you started:

- Address
- Phone numbers
- Email
- Pre-Med?
- Insurance information such as Social Security number, birth date, employer name and address, policy number
- Recent x-rays/records
- Quote a fee range for appointment scheduled
- Give good directions to the office

Conflict Resolution

Sometimes, no matter how well prepared you are, patients throw you a curve ball in the form of an objection, concern, or disagreement. For example, if the patient says, "I thought my insurance covered 100 percent! I didn't think I'd have to pay anything," you have two choices:

you can argue with the person or empathize and reach an understanding. Whenever you are faced with a contentious situation, there are a few good rules to remember:

- **Being right is wrong.** Don't worry about needing to be right. Worry more about understanding than being understood. In other words, acknowledge patients' confusion and frustration. They thought they understood one thing about their insurance coverage and now you are telling them something completely different. It really doesn't matter that you are absolutely right. We would likely feel the same way if roles were reversed. In addition, it is difficult to remain upset with someone who is agreeing with you. Start your response to their distress with an empathetic statement that demonstrates you understand and relate to their feelings. For example, *"I don't blame you for being irritated about this news, Mrs. Jones. I can fully appreciate how frustrating it must be to have understood one thing about your coverage only to find out something different from us. This has to be confusing for you to say the least!"*

- **Use "and" instead of "but."** When you begin to launch into your defense or explanation, remember to avoid the connector words "but" or "however." A better choice would be the word "and." To continue the example above: *"This has to be confusing for you to say the least AND we won't really know your exact coverage until we get the necessary insurance information."* It sounds very different if we say: *"This has to be confusing for you to say the least BUT we won't really know your exact coverage until we get the necessary insurance information."* If we use the words "but" or "however" they act as silent erasers to the previous statements.

- **Don't be overly attached to the outcome.** Be more concerned about giving patients all the relevant information in a clear, motivational, and objective manner. Assure them that you are confident they will make the best choice for their life and that you respect that fully. If they say that this just won't work for them, then respect that choice unemotionally, treat them with dignity, and help them find someone who could better meet their needs. I recommend always keeping telephone numbers for your local dental society or dental school close at hand. Remember, their situation may change and you want them to remember their interaction with you kindly.

It's not that we don't care if we schedule the patient or not. Rather we are communicating from a place of confidence. There are no winners or losers here. We have listened to them, understood their feelings, and offered solutions that will hopefully work best for both parties. Then the decision is theirs, and we as dental professionals must respect their choice.

- **Push yourself relentlessly to improve your communication skills.** Always be working to improve your batting average just a little bit more. Do your very best to make sure that patients know that we want them as our patients. But you won't get everyone nor should you. Not every caller is a good fit for your practice. Continue to analyze your ability to convert prospective new patients to appointments. Meet them in their world and guide them to the best place for their needs. And you will speak with a confidence, kindness, and lack of judgment that the patient will definitely feel.

In summary, there are four keys to thinking differently about new patient phone calls:

1. **Stop using the computer screen to guide your call.** Instead, memorize the four steps of a great call (below) along with the transitional statements, or create a new patient call intake slip that helps to guide the call using the Four-Step Formula.

2. **Memorize the Four Steps to a Great Call**, not a script.
   - *Connection:* Make a quick but powerful personal connection.
   - *Questions:* Ask questions that help identify what the caller most wants to solve or obtain.
   - *Solutions:* Offer the best solution based on what you've learned from your questions. Remember to enthusiastically sell your doctor and practice, but only as they relate to the

concerns or desires expressed by the patient.

- *Details:* Get the details necessary to process the patient's information and provide an effective and efficient appointment.

3. **Memorize three transition statements to move through the Four Step process easily.**

   - Transition from Connection to Questioning:

     I want to give you the right information (appointment). Would you mind if I asked you a few questions first?

   - Transition from Questioning to Solution:

     So Mrs. Jones, the most important things to you are... Then I believe the best solution (appointment) would be ... Let me tell you why I believe this is a perfect fit for you...

   - Transition from Solutions to Details:

     I know you are going to be so glad that you came to see Dr. Smith. Now, may I get a few details that will help us make your visit go even more smoothly?

4. **Be authentically you.** Be confident. Be gracious. Be enthusiastic. Be You.

In the end, there are two critical ingredients that create a great phone call: 1) possessing the skills to know where you are going with the call, and 2) the level of sincere enthusiasm and personal concern you convey to the caller. Your enthusiasm and attitude are more powerful than any words you could ever use.

You take several of these calls a day. The potential patient may make one of these calls every five years or so. Every call is a chance to help someone resolve a problem and see a great dentist. So, beef up your skills and crank up your enthusiasm for the next call you take. You can do it. And the results will speak for themselves!

ABOUT KATHERINE EITEL

Katherine Eitel is an experienced communications coach in the dental and discretionary healthcare fields. Katherine's revolutionary phone skills training and Phone Skills Training Call Service have helped hundreds of practices improve marketing results, professional image, and the bottom line. Her training programs appeal to all adult learning styles. She utilizes interactive exercises and testing components that help participants truly connect to the subject, ensuring they embrace the message and apply it long after their training session. Katherine is proud to serve as President of the Academy of Dental Management Consultants for 2006-2008. She is also an active member of the National Speakers Association and Speaking Consulting Network. For more information on Phone Skills Training or Communications Training for the entire team, or to book Katherine as a speaker for her Think Differently Presentation Series, call (800) 595-7060 or visit her website at www.KatherineEitel.com.

Contact Information:
Katherine Eitel
Katherine Eitel and Associates
P.O. Box 50490
Mesa, AZ 85208
Phone: (800) 595-7060
Fax: (480) 275-2204
Email: info@KatherineEitel.com
Website: www.KatherineEitel.com

DENTAL MARKETING AND YOUR PATIENT'S PERCEPTION

by Judy Goldman

In today's unpredictable economy there is a common concern in the dental industry. Since dental treatment is optional, in the opinion of the general public, the current key word in our profession is marketing. Coaches and consultants are recommending marketing and business promotion as a must for their clients since new patient numbers are critical to the success of a dental practice. Like dentistry itself, postponing the marketing/promotion process can result in more painful and costly solutions.

"Laura, call the phone company. I think we need to increase the size of our Yellow Page ad, and find out how much it costs to put one of those coupons in that monthly mailer. Maybe we could run a special on veneers this month. What did they teach me about marketing in dental school, anyway?" Does this sound familiar? Without a specialized background in marketing, the typical dentist has no clue how to develop a successful marketing plan. There are certain areas of healthcare promotion that need a deft touch, and if handled incorrectly, will cause more harm than good.

There is a public belief that there are three different types of dental practices: the big discount dental clinic, the smaller, more personal clinic, and the private practice. As with everything in life, perception is reality. Regardless of your notion of reality and the time and money invested in creating your vision in the practice, what patients perceive to be true represents fact in their minds. Therefore, when creating the dream practice that promotes business with the patient types you select, care must be taken to include those patients' perceptions in the design. It would also be important to recognize that not all consumers shop the same way. Sam Walton created an extremely successful empire by marketing to a specific target. So did the creators of Nordstroms. Both were right in their design and plan. Dentists must do the same, so if you are looking for the customers who shop at Saks Fifth Avenue, don't advertise with a "blue light special."

Mindful planning is essential before setting any marketing plan into action, and establishing a target market is step one. Decide whom you want as your patients and design the plan to attract them. This process begins with a demographic survey of your existing patient base. Determine your favorite types of patients by reflecting on the people who are current patients in the practice and those who refer their friends. In addition, research the population living and working in your immediate area. If your practice were located in an underprivileged area with low income families, it would be harder to promote to higher income patients.

Not all marketing is designed to bring in new patients. There are four different components that affect practice growth, and each one can greatly increase the practice bottom line without increasing the actual number of patients.

1. Increase the available procedures in the practice. Don't be left behind in this rapidly advancing profession. It's important to be up-to-date on all possible beneficial treatments available to your patients, including optional cosmetic, implant, and preventive treatment. Most people today place a high value on good health, and if they understand the benefits and consequences, will accept the best option when given that choice.

It has been reported that the majority of dental litigation stems from failure to diagnose and treat: more specifically, periodontal neglect. This fact alone should prompt you to carry an effective and profitable hygiene department. The ADA has reported that 70 percent of the adult population has some form of periodontal disease. It follows that a large portion of your patients should be in some form of periodontal treatment and maintenance. Therefore, it is not true that the hygiene department need be a loss leader.

2. Present and complete more comprehensive cases. Treatment planning and case presentations are the most critical component in the business of dentistry. It would be pointless to open your office door each day if you were not selling dentistry.

Consumers today will buy only what they want with their discretionary dollars and, like it or not, dentistry is discretionary. Unfortunately, we compete with much more desirable products. For this reason, it is vitally important to know what your customer wants and the best method of presentation.

The process begins with understanding, and helping to improve, the patient's dental values. Determine the values' baseline during the initial visit before beginning the examination. Have an open discussion about concerns and expectations, then open more opportunities by sharing information about advances and benefits of dentistry today. This is not a teaching session, but a conversation specific to each patient. Look at it from the patient's perception, and know that if you are not excited about dentistry, the patient won't be.

Once you and the patient have clearly established the ultimate and long-term dental objectives, present all treatment recommendations as they apply specifically to accomplishing what the patient wants. Learn to use the word "want" instead of "need" when discussing treatment plans. *"In order to create that smile you wanted, you're going to want to whiten your teeth and change those discolored fillings in the back with tooth-colored crowns. This procedure will even out the alignment in addition to brightening the color of your teeth."*

Discovering and overcoming any barriers that prevent patients from accepting treatment need to be addressed, and the cost of treatment will almost always be a concern. Offering a variety of ways of affording treatment promotes acceptance, and since we are entering into a long-term relationship with patients, offering to phase treatment over time is another way to help accomplish what the patient wants. It is not always necessary to offer in-house financing since there is a plethora of credit cards available. Outside funding is the same way today's consumers finance other discretionary items.

Present optimum dental treatment, even when you don't think your patient can afford it. Time and time again, dentists are surprised by what patients can and will buy. Each person places a different value on dental care. Because someone may not have the funds does not mean that the interest is not there. If the desire is there, a person will usually find the means to afford dental care, and it is an injustice to not present optimum treatment to everyone.

The fear of pain can be a big problem to some people when thinking about dental treatment. Ask if there are any concerns about the treatment recommendations so that pain can be eliminated as a source of worry for your patient. A painless injection is the best marketing tool any dentist can have. Be honest with yourself, and if you are not sure you are "painless," ask your patients and your staff, but be prepared to improve some techniques if the reports are negative.

With today's pace, everyone is rushing everywhere, and many people will be more concerned about the time investment than the money. Respect these concerns and the importance they play in the accepting of the dental treatment. Some patients prefer to have fewer but longer appointments, and they will appreciate your consideration.

3. Create a more productive continuing care program. Pre-booked hygiene patients return to the practice about 1.3 times per year. The average active patient who receives only a reminder card returns less than once a year for continuing care appointments. Typically, the recall card is filed away with the intention to call when there is more time and/or money available. It is not uncommon for these patients to be lost from the practice for two years. In the meantime, they are available for the next great dental coupon that arrives in their mail, or maybe referred to another dentist by a friend.

It is also crucial for your patient to have a specific and personal reason for the next visit. *"John, everything looks fine. We'll send you a card in six months."* Chances are you won't see him in six months. *"Sylvia, I need to see you in January, since I am concerned about your gum tissues. Your periodontal health looks good right now, but it is important to monitor this condition."* Sylvia has a specific reason to return in January, while John probably will postpone his maintenance appointment until he feels the need himself.

4. Increase the number of new patients coming into the practice.

One of the reasons most dentists are not successful marketing themselves and their practice is that they are not completely sure what dental marketing is. It might help to break it down into the three separate areas of internal, external, and public relations.

Internal marketing creates the image projected by the dental practice. It is the least expensive advertising that brings in the majority of your prized patients. A healthy practice relies on this promotion for 80 to 85 percent of its new patients. It will encompass everything from the first telephone contact to all of the service-oriented systems that keep you looking special to your existing patients. Also included here are your internal marketing tools, such as the office brochure, logo, letterhead, and all correspondence from you and your office. Your appearance, and that of your office and staff (including the uniforms, office décor, grooming and lack of clutter), will determine the initial image perceived by your patients. As you have heard many times before, first impressions are the most important. It may not seem fair to be judged on your choice of gown, but we cannot always expect life to be fair.

Internal communication is paramount in your internal marketing and should be a common goal shared by the entire team. The slightest discord will prevent success. If your office staff is not all moving in the same direction, take immediate steps to correct this hindrance. Staff meetings and morning huddles promote communication and teamwork. Warm and friendly patient communication is also required, and if the dentist is not naturally comfortable bonding in a not-clinical way with patients, staff will need to be excessive in this area. A dentist with a reserved personality can create and present an image of clinical expertise, and your patients will be very comfortable as long as they are receiving the personal commitment from the staff.

External Marketing should be considered only after you have a consistent and comfortable internal marketing technique. There is certainly nothing wrong with letting the public know you are welcoming new patients, but carefully design your advertising pieces to project the quality image established by you and your staff.

There are two distinctly different types of advertising and knowing the difference can save lots of money. Direct marketing has an offer and a deadline. When done as a mailer, the resident must open and read the piece, and it must compete with everyone else who is advertising through the post office. In order to be successful it must include these three most important elements: a quality mailing list, a desirable and competitive offer, and an overall appeal that will get the piece noticed.

Remember that mass advertising and cut-rate offers will bring warm bodies into a dental office, but it will also bring bargain shoppers. Coupon patients will take your special offer and wait for the next coupon. Statistics show that discount offers will also promote more work, but less profit, since a higher overhead is needed to run the volume. Start-up practices can use this type of marketing to jumpstart business, but know that not all patients will stay with the practice long term.

Image marketing makes no offer. Advertising pieces that use this technique must project a desirable image that is intended to be recognizable and remembered by the prospective patient. Repeating these ads over time is a key element in their success. Most often, you would find this type of marketing used in newsletters, newspapers, and magazines. Remember the importance of using the medium most likely to be viewed by your target marketing. Consistency is required.

Public Relations Marketing is the third area of marketing. Your membership in clubs and service organizations, public service and affiliations of any sort, will let the public know who you are. Most patients have little clinical knowledge to judge the quality of their dentistry, and will choose their dentist because of his or the staff's personality, chairside manner, or public image. Don't hesitate to use all opportunities to bring your good name into public view.

The Four P's of Marketing

Before we can create a complete marketing plan, we must examine the four basic quadrants of marketing and evaluate where your office stands in each area. This is part of the preliminary research that will point you in the right direction and help avoid costly and time-consuming mistakes.

Product—The patient's perceived value.

Since there is really no way for the average patient to evaluate the actual quality of the dentistry itself, in this area we are dealing with the patient's perception of quality and service.

Price—The overall perception of the fees charged and participation in reduced fee insurance plans.

We must consider the participation in PPO and Managed Care Plans as part of our marketing since the whole purpose of such participation is to enlist new patients. We also inspire referrals from the patient's opinion of our fees.

Place—The location and visibility of the facility.

By having a convenient location with visible signage, prospective patients can choose their new dentist according to convenience, which includes parking and accessibility.

Promotion—The actual internal marketing, advertising, and public relations involved in promoting the practice.

The following marketing audit can help in deciding where to focus when creating your marketing plan. Have the entire team help in answering each of these questions. Choose the answer that most closely approximates the condition of your practice.

Product

1. We offer 5-Star services in our dental office.
   a. Always
   b. Almost always
   c. Often
   d. Seldom
   e. Never
2. Our patients perceive the quality of dental service received here as
   a. Excellent
   b. Above average
   c. Average
   d. Acceptable
   e. Not that great
3. Our patients are left waiting in the reception area and treatment room
   a. Less than 5 minutes
   b. 5 to 10 minutes
   c. 10 to 15 minutes
   d. 15 to 20 minutes
   e. Over 20 minutes
4. Our patients receive a personal greeting from everyone in the office they come in contact with.
   a. Always
   b. Almost always
   c. Often
   d. Seldom
   e. Never
5. We treat each other with courtesy and respect.
   a. Always
   b. Almost always
   c. Often
   d. Seldom
   e. Never

6. Our patients understand their treatment needs and have the opportunity to ask questions.
   a. Always
   b. Almost always
   c. Often
   d. Seldom
   e. Never

7. Our patients complete a signed financial agreement before any treatment is performed.
   a. Always
   b. Almost always
   c. Often
   d. Seldom
   e. Never

8. Our clinical treatment is painless.
   a. Always
   b. Almost always
   c. Often
   d. Seldom
   e. Never

9. Our percentage of new patients referred from our existing patients is
   a. 100%
   b. 80 to 100%
   c. 70 to 80%
   d. 50 to 70%
   e. Under 50%

10. Our patients know that we are unique and that they would have difficulty finding what we offer in another practice.
    a. Absolutely
    b. Mostly
    c. Probably
    d. Probably not
    e. No

Price

1. Our fees are reasonable.
   a. Absolutely
   b. Mostly
   c. Probably
   d. Probably not
   e. No
2. Our patients perceive the fees as reasonable.
   a. Always
   b. Usually
   c. Sometimes
   d. Rarely
   e. Never
3. Patients in our practice are fully informed about the fees they are charged prior to beginning treatment.
   a. Always
   b. Usually
   c. Sometimes
   d. Rarely
   e. Never
4. Payment options are flexible and there are several different ways to arrange payments.
   a. Always
   b. Usually
   c. Sometimes
   d. Rarely
   e. Never
5. Our patients have committed to the treatment before the financial negotiation begins.
   a. Always
   b. Usually
   c. Sometimes
   d. Rarely
   e. Never

6. We enthusiastically offer information and assist our patients with their insurance.
    a. Always
    b. Usually
    c. Sometimes
    d. Rarely
    e. Never

7. We accept reduced fee PPO insurance plans.
    a. All of them
    b. Almost all of them
    c. Many of them
    d. A select few that fall within our guidelines
    e. None

8. We participate in managed care plans.
    a. All of them
    b. Almost all of them
    c. Many of them
    d. A select few that fall within our guidelines
    e. None

9. We are comfortable discussing money with patients.
    a. Very comfortable
    b. Somewhat comfortable
    c. We're okay
    d. Somewhat uncomfortable
    e. No

10. We get patient complaints about accounting and insurance billing.
    a. Never
    b. Seldom
    c. Sometimes
    d. Often
    e. All the time

Place

1. Our office décor is pleasant and comfortable.
   a. Absolutely
   b. Mostly
   c. Somewhat
   d. Not really
   e. No
2. We have plenty of space and do not appear to be crowded.
   a. Absolutely
   b. Mostly
   c. Somewhat
   d. Not really
   e. No
3. The office interior has plenty of light.
   a. Absolutely
   b. Mostly
   c. Somewhat
   d. Not really
   e. No
4. Our office is thoroughly clean.
   a. Absolutely
   b. Mostly
   c. Somewhat
   d. Not really
   e. No
5. Our office is visible to the general public.
   a. Absolutely
   b. Mostly
   c. Somewhat
   d. Not really
   e. No

6. The outside sign projects a clean and clear image of our practice.
    a. Absolutely
    b. Mostly
    c. Somewhat
    d. Not really
    e. No
7. The area in which our office is located has a good reputation.
    a. Absolutely
    b. Mostly
    c. Somewhat
    d. Not really
    e. No
8. We provide enough parking spaces for our patients.
    a. Absolutely
    b. Mostly
    c. Somewhat
    d. Not really
    e. No
9. It is easy to give and follow directions to our office.
    a. Absolutely
    b. Mostly
    c. Somewhat
    d. Not really
    e. No
10. The number of new patients who find our office by driving or walking by is
    a. Over 80%
    b. 60 to 80%
    c. 40 to 60%
    d. 20 to 40%
    e. Less than 20%

Promotion

1. We ask our patient for referrals.
   a. Always
   b. Almost always
   c. Sometimes
   d. Seldom
   e. Never
2. We have a clearly defined image and logo printed on all office forms.
   a. Absolutely
   b. Mostly
   c. Somewhat
   d. Not really
   e. No
3. We send a welcome packet, including our practice brochure, to all new patients.
   a. Always
   b. Usually
   c. Sometimes
   d. Rarely
   e. Never
4. The doctor and team are socially active and visible in the community.
   a. Always
   b. Usually
   c. Sometimes
   d. Rarely
   e. Never
5. We have a referral reward system for showing our appreciation.
   a. Always
   b. Usually
   c. Sometimes
   d. Rarely
   e. Never

6. We communicate regularly by mail with our patients via newsletters, information letters, and cards.
   a. Always
   b. Usually
   c. Sometimes
   d. Rarely
   e. Never

7. We have a great Yellow Page ad.
   a. Absolutely
   b. Mostly
   c. Somewhat
   d. Not really
   e. No

8. We each have our own business cards or "smile cards" and pass them out liberally.
   a. Always
   b. Usually
   c. Sometimes
   d. Rarely
   e. Never

9. We do direct mail, radio, and print advertising.
   a. Always
   b. Sometimes
   c. Usually
   d. Rarely
   e. Never

10. The percentage of new patients coming into our office from paid advertising is
    a. Over 80%
    b. 60 to 80%
    c. 40 to 60%
    d. 20 to 40%
    e. Less than 20%

Total the number of each letter in each category and give the following values: A=4 points B=3 points C=2 points D=1 point E=0 points.

Values	A=4	B=3	C=2	D=1	E=0	Total
Product						
Price						
Place						
Promotion						

Grand Total Points _____

The 4P's Marketing Graph

The Grand Total Points equals 100% of your marketing pie chart.

Score for Product _____ divided by the TOTAL = _____%

Score for Price _____ divided by the TOTAL = _____%

Score for Place _____ divided by the TOTAL = _____%

Score for Promotion _____ divided by the TOTAL = _____%

Equals 100%

Fill in the percentages of each 'P' to complete the comparison.

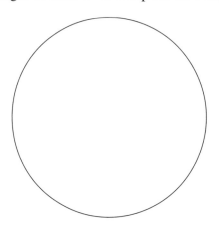

Example

Values	A=4	B=3	C=2	D=1	E=0	Total
Product	2x4 (value)=8	2x3=6	3x2=6	2x1=2	1x0=0	22
Price	0x4=0	1x3=3	6x2=12	2x1=2	2x0=0	17
Place	6x4=24	3x3=9	1x2=2	0x1=0	0x0=0	35
Promotion	5x4=20	5x3=15	0x2=0	0x1=0	0x0=0	35

Grand Total Points _____ 109

The 4P's Marketing Graph

The Grand Total Points equals 100% of your marketing pie chart.

Score for Product	22	divided by the TOTAL (109) =	20%
Score for Price	17	divided by the TOTAL =	16%
Score for Place	35	divided by the TOTAL =	32%
Score for Promotion	35	divided by the TOTAL =	32%

Equals 100%

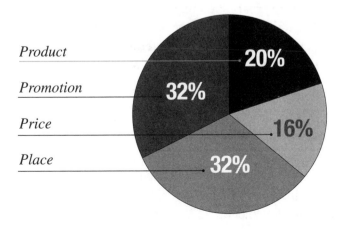

Since each dental office is different, it is important to understand that there is no right or wrong mix. This is simply the baseline from which you can build your own marketing plan. Understanding your current mix is a good starting point.

The amount of funding dedicated to your marketing should depend on several different factors. Some experts recommend investing a percentage of the estimated or expected increase in production. With this equation, if you expected to increase your income by $100,000 next year, your investment could be as much as $20,000 (20%) or $1,700 per month toward practice promotion. Here, a 5:1 return on investment for marketing projects is expected.

Using another formula, allocate between 3 and 10 percent of average monthly collections for marketing. The percentage would depend on how aggressive your marketing needs are. An established practice looking for stability and slight growth would invest 3 percent, while the new doctor starting out would spend much more.

Once you've determined the budget, it's time to create the plan.
1. Set specific goals
   a. Increase available services and/or procedures
   b. Present and complete more comprehensive cases
   c. Create a productive continuing care program
   d. Bring new patients into the practice
2. Set a plan for Internal Marketing
   a. Schedule training in exceptional communication
   b. Set a plan for inspiring patient referrals
3. Plan your external marketing (staying within the budget)
   a. Determine budget
   b. Clarify target marketing
   c. Initiate marketing using the best method within your budget
4. Get famous in the community
5. Monitor results
   a. Track referral source of every new patient
   b. Monitor income from each source and compare cost for return-on-investment

c. Adjust marketing as analysis suggests

With the average practice losing patients at a rate of 20 percent a year, you do need to attract new patients to your practice, but be careful how you do it. Your marketing campaign, if done carefully, will bring you values-based patients. If done carelessly, it will bring chaos.

Step away from the dental perspective and create your plan for growth with the patient in mind. Then, remember the two key phrases in promotion, fund it and schedule it.

Dream the dream, create the vision, build the castle, but be sure to keep your eye on the target in the process.

ABOUT JUDY GOLDMAN

*J*udy Goldman started her dental career at the age of 16 working as an assistant for her father (Dr. Speedy Nutz) and has, since then, worked in every corner of the dental practice. As the wife of a dentist, she brings over 35 years of practical experience to the field of Dental Consulting with understanding from both the team's and the business owner's perspective. She has added to this solid foundation an education in Business Administration and Marketing. This combination of practical hands-on experience, education, and business acumen has given Judy a unique perspective on the professional challenges of building a solid business and marketing program for the successful dental practice. This has made her a much sought-after educator, lecturer, and author on the subject of practice administration and the start-up and organization of dental practices. It was Judy's privilege to be listed in Dentistry Today as one of the industry's "Leaders in Dental Consulting." Whether your need is a solid foundation or a revitalized existing practice, Judy Goldman and Practice Development Associates understand your dream.

Contact Information:
Judy Goldman
Practice Development Associates
81 Cook Court
Chula Vista, CA 91910
Phone: (619) 691-7990
Email: Judy@PDA-JudyGoldman.com
Website: www.PDA-JudyGoldman.com

DON'T BECOME
A STATISTIC:
Prevent Embezzlement of Your Profits

by Pauline Grabowski

Today, one of several challenges that all business owners face is employee management. We are going to discuss those challenges and how to take appropriate measures to prevent and detect a possible embezzlement in your workplace. Statistics show that two out of three practices have had some form of theft, whether it has involved documentation of hours worked, office supplies, petty cash, or practice revenue. Is embezzlement a crime? Absolutely, "Embezzlement is a fraudulent conversion of property of another or by a person in lawful possession of the property." Is this crime punishable by law? You bet it is and any individual who deems it necessary to take something that does not belong to him should be prosecuted. As a consultant for the health care industry, it is my role to help my clients' business by implementing systems for prevention of theft.

A business will thrive when the owner and team members have a common goal. The goal is to have a leader who maintains a system of structure and balance for the business. This structure includes practice management tools that are learned and implemented by the owner and team members. The systems for success are Communications (among owner, team members, and patients); Hiring a Winning Team (motivated, enthusiastic, goal oriented); Accountability (defined job descriptions, checks and balances by report on a daily, weekly, and monthly basis, scheduling for productivity, tracking production/collections, accounts receivable management, case acceptance); Marketing Guidelines (target your identity, practice brochures, newsletters); Clinical Skills (owner and clinical team members); Team Development (building a great team of individuals who strive for success) and Patient Retention (continuing care protocol). A practice will profit when all systems are working. When a breakdown occurs in any of these systems, a practice should evaluate how and why the system is not working. This active response could result in the prevention of misappropriations of funds.

Why People Embezzle

Surely most individuals understand that it is wrong to steal or to take something that does not belong to them. There usually is a motive behind someone's decision to steal. People may find themselves in need of money, due to financial problems resulting from a spouse's layoff, living beyond their means, or a feeling that they are owed more compensation. People often embezzle due to behavior traits, including addictive behaviors, attitude and/or lifestyle issues, lack of personal integrity, and desire for personal gain.

He/She Was a Trusted Employee

Instilling value in people is one thing and trusting is another. As business owners we all try to take all the appropriate measures to hire the right people. There are certain criteria to look for in people when hiring a winning team. As the owner and leader of your business, set the tone by empowering people.

The Four Basic Leadership Styles

Employees who benefit from each style are described:
1. Directing: Because this style focuses on structure, organization, and supervision, it works with people who, although enthusiastic and committed, lack competence.
2. Coaching: This style uses direction and support to lead people who have some competence but lack commitment.
3. Supporting: Competent people who lack confidence and motivation benefit from a leader who provides praise.

4. Delegating: When people are competent and committed, they are willing and able to work independently. A leader can turn over much of the day-to-day decision making to this group.

The keys to successful leadership are to hire the right people and spend quality time training them to do their jobs and to educate the team members to understand how your practice operates. Once the right person has been hired for the position, provide comprehensive job description which clearly defines accountability to the practice. Then define office policy by presenting a Personnel Policy Manual to the individual. I highly recommend Bent Ericksen & Associates, who specialize in employment law compliance and human resources management, as a resource for creating and maintaining policy manuals. It is imperative that you familiarize yourself with the state and federal laws for hiring and employing individuals in your business. How many times have we as business owners developed material only to find out that it requires revision time after time? As a consultant and business owner, I decided not to reinvent the wheel over and over again, so I became certified with Bent Ericksen & Associates to offer my clients assistance with compliancy to the healthcare industry. Now I know that my clients have the necessary tools for human resource compliancy as well as the proper forms that are required to operate their business.

About three years ago, one of the dentists in my hometown contacted me to discuss some apparent changes in practice revenue from the previous year to the current year. The doctor stated that there were some discrepancies in her practice revenue that showed fewer collections this year than the prior year. The practice had a thirty percent increase in production during the year in question, and she could not understand why the collections were down so much from the previous year. She told me that there were some suspicions stemming from a front office team member's bragging to other team members that she had enrolled her daughter in dance and ballet classes as well as gymnastics. (Of course, the worker had mentioned to the team earlier that her household income would not warrant any extracurricular activities for her daughter.) So the doctor was suspicious. We will call this individual Jane, for privacy purposes. Jane decided to take advantage of the doctor by embezzling approximately $75,000 over the course of a year. This theft occurred when the practice was obviously growing, but the doctor was very busy with balancing the ownership of a business and a new family all at the same time. Since Jane's personal financial well-being was being altered at home to the degree that she could not offer her daughter the extracurricular activities, she decided to implement a system of her own, which consisted of altering the practice write-offs to her benefit. For example, a patient would come into the practice for treatment and present Optima Insurance coverage. At the time, Optima Insurance allocated a 10 percent courtesy to the patient on all treatments performed since the practice is a participating provider. When a patient paid cash for a portion of the services rendered, Jane would make an adjustment to include the cash payment. She was also making Optima write-offs for patients that did not even carry the Optima plan. So where were the red flags here? The write-offs and no cash payments. Where were the systems in place to measure? The only system was "trust." Did it work for the practice? No. Should the practice have used some preventive measures? Absolutely. Sometimes the job of a good embezzler is to become the trusted employee.

Ten Red Flags

An employee who is stealing from the business will probably exhibit one or more of the following behaviors:

1. Does not want anyone to do her/his job.
2. Holds daily work over to next day.
3. Prefers to work unsupervised.
4. Works after hours or takes work home.
5. Does not want to take vacations.
6. Points finger at other team members.
7. Has no explanation for mistakes.
8. Asks owner to sign checks while treating patients.
9. Has a financial lifestyle change.
10. Documents unexplainable business expenses.

Some other symptoms:

- Frequently requests cash advances or does not repay prior loans.
- Receives telephone calls at work from creditors.
- Wages are being garnished.
- Frequently tardy or fails to report to work and poorly explained absences.
- Gambles at the workplace or refers to excessive gambling activities.
- Often has a hangover, or references excessive drinking behavior.
- References excessive use of recreational drugs.
- Preoccupied with family, marital or personal financial stresses.
- Meets questionable people at work.
- Displays disruptive or erratic behavior, is often withdrawn, angry, frustrated, and exhibits mood swings.

So how do we as business owners prevent this kind of challenge from disrupting what we have all worked so hard to accomplish? To prevent is to prevail. I cannot stress enough the importance of the guidelines below. These measures will guide you as you take steps to prevent becoming an embezzlement statistic.

Prevention Guidelines

1. When hiring a team member, always investigate every employee with a background check and have the appropriate information on the employment application. (Please reference Bent Ericksen & Associates for forms.)
2. Contact prior employers for references.
3. Develop written comprehensive job descriptions for accountability.
4. Define user passwords on practice management software programs with designated security levels.
5. Review day sheets from software program daily to make sure that all patients were entered with treatment performed.
6. Balance and make deposits daily.
7. Periodically review the work of every employee, especially those serving a bookkeeping function.

8. Insist that all employees take vacations as outlined in the policy manual.
9. Review collection records and accounts receivable balances daily.
10. Mandate in the policy manual that all write-offs over $100 have to be approved by the owner.
11. Compare write-offs with cash receipts.
12. If possible, recommend the owner should make deposits to the bank.
13. Use a practice stamp "For Deposit Only" to be placed on all patient checks received.
14. Conduct audits at irregular intervals on scheduling, accounts receivable, day sheets/reconciliations of deposits. Let employees know that the practice conducts these audits.
15. Review audit trails on software programs weekly, if not daily, to identify changes or deletions on patient records.
16. Keep a petty cash fund of only $50-$100 on hand and maintain a register in a locked cash drawer with a running tally of items purchased or cash transactions.
17. HIRE A CONSULTANT/ACCOUNTANT to review financial records. They are the experts who can determine red flags.

Other measures to prevent embezzlement

As business owners we are all faced with the challenges of finding and keeping good employees. In the past five years this difficulty has increased due to the changing economy and entrepreneurs' leaving companies to open their own businesses. It has been my experience that you have to work extremely hard to find exceptional people in the work force. I believe networking and communicating with other businesses will help immensely to find the right person for your environment. A warm, caring establishment should attract warm and caring people. Remember that the appropriate measures have to be taken to hire a winning team and to maintain a healthy working environment. Understanding the human element will empower you to manage people. Another way to measure your employees is by implementing patient surveys. Most patients are reluctant to express their concerns to doctors or team members, but will give an opinion to a third party questionnaire. I work with a company called Valmont Research. Valmont will help a business measure its success by presenting a questionnaire to patients. What are issues that often concern a patient? Confusing financial policies, lack of discussion of fees prior to treatment, lack of courtesy and professionalism in addressing financial issues. Well patient surveys can assist the business owner to regularly assess patient satisfaction and perceptions of the practice, as well as identify trouble spots so they can be addressed quickly. These surveys will assist the owner in learning of deficiencies and discrepancies in the business, too. What a valuable tool!

Accounting measures to prevent theft

1. Doctor has main password.
2. Others have separate passwords with defined security levels.
3. Employee reports weekly and monthly On Time.
4. Compare day sheets to deposit slips and income entries in QuickBooks®.
5. Petty cash receipts must equal amount to be replenished.
6. Always personally sign checks, no stamps.
7. Watch vendor supply expenses and know vendor companies.
8. Pay attention to patient reimbursements.
9. Use the "Audit Trail" feature in QuickBooks®.
10. Get Organized!

References & Resources

QuickBooks® 2005 In Your Practice, Susan Gunn
Valmont Research
http://criminal-law.freeadvice.com
www.agd.org
www.cds.org
www.premierdentalconsulting.com

ABOUT PAULINE GRABOWSKI

Pauline Grabowski's diverse experience in dentistry includes work as a certified dental auxiliary, a practice administrator, and a systems analyst. Pauline has accumulated a wealth of knowledge over the past 24 years and has shared it with hundreds of dental practices. As a professional consultant, Pauline provides personalized healthcare solutions to meet the specific needs of every healthcare practice. In addition to her speaking engagements, Pauline provides on-site analysis and consulting. She specializes in new office design and setup, marketing, scheduling for productivity, treatment planning, case acceptance, and team development. Pauline is a member of the Academy of Dental Management Consultants, Speaking/Consulting Network and is currently a sponsor for AGD Fellowship/Mastership credit, which allows for CEU's.

Contact information:
Pauline Grabowski
Pauline Grabowski & Associates
P.O. Box 15528
Chesapeake, VA 23328-5528
Phone: (757) 497-2040
Fax: (757) 482-7047
Cell: (757) 560-0667
Email: pg@paulinegrabowski.com
Website: www.paulinegrabowski.com

START ON THE RIGHT FOOT
WITH NEW STAFF ORIENTATION

by Larry M. Guzzardo

Have you ever entered a door only to find out you were in the wrong place? Maybe the hall closet instead of your bedroom? Do you remember how that felt? Imagine new staff members; would you want them to feel as if they had made a mistake? The feeling will not go away all by itself. If a new staff member has an uncertain perception of what is expected, it is going to cost your practice in many different ways: lost productivity and confusion by your current staff that can never be recovered, time you could more profitably spend running your practice, and the domino effect of even one negative person dragging down the performance of others. Taking steps to create a positive environment for your new staff member will reduce stress in the practice and create a smooth transition for a long-term relationship. Whether staff members are new to dentistry, your practice, or changing departments, their productivity can be enhanced with a thorough orientation program.

New staff orientation is the bridge that takes the new staff member from the old way of doing things to the new way. Starting on the right foot encourages the new staff members' desire to improve performance, teamwork, participation, and learning. Including an orientation as part of the training schedule helps new staff members understand what is expected of them in their new office and why. Your orientation should give those who come to work in your practice the opportunity to realize the good choice they made in deciding to work for you. Not after they have assumed their new responsibilities, but before. A proper orientation makes people feel comfortable in a new environment.

How well your new staff members are able to assimilate the teamwork in your office should not only depend on them, but on how well teamwork is communicated to them at the beginning of your working relationship. The new staff member orientation is how you communicate this expectation to them. What are the new staff member's most important needs? First, knowledge of the doctor's philosophy about dentistry, a training program, and an understanding of the procedures performed by the doctor. When staff members have knowledge of the doctor's philosophy of dentistry, they can professionally represent the doctor and the practice to patients by intelligently answering questions. Do not forget, they also need to know the specialists you commonly refer your patients to and why. Second, an understanding of the relationship between the hygiene, chair-side, and business office staff. The new staff member should know the responsibility assigned to each area and the line of communication. Third, the staff member must know what the doctor expects from him or her.

The orientation should include the following activities:

- Discuss changes you have noticed in dentistry.
- Suggest ways the new staff member can use departmental and general staff meetings to transfer training experiences to the new office.
- Acknowledge that adapting to a new work environment will require adjustments.
- Encourage and remind your new staff members to consider each other as experienced resources.
- Allow new staff members to openly discuss any questions or concerns.
- Complete employment forms; complete new employee checklist.
- Learn job description.
- Review training schedule.
- Review OSHA guidelines.
- Meet individually with each staff member.

Knowing the relationship between departments and their specific areas of responsibility helps new staff members understand the importance of their individual responsibilities and how the quality of their work affects others. Understanding how staff members relate to each other is one of the most critical elements in building a sense of comfort with a new position, job satisfaction, and productivity. Finally, staff members need clearly defined expectations of what is expected of them in terms of results, problem solving, and decision making.

Structure the orientation program to introduce the new staff member to the practice and set the training schedule before the new staff member arrives. Doctors should be prepared with basic equipment, supplies, job aids, and keys to the office. Then, provide a tour of the office, which should include introductions to co-workers and a short explanation of their responsibilities. Ideally, time should be allotted for the new employee to have brief interviews with co-workers as a way to become acquainted with them.

Doctors can reduce anxiety in new staff members by assigning a co-worker to act as a coach. New staff members will welcome the chance to create long-term bonds of loyalty with you or another member of the staff, especially in a world where we have come to distrust bonds of loyalty with established organizations and the government. Taking this step boosts morale, develops trust, uncovers hidden strengths, and eliminates resentment and fear. The coach can answer questions, make other introductions, and give informal advice. Coaches also help new staff by informing them about how work gets done or how problems are resolved. Pick a staff member with good people skills to be the new staff member's coach. This person can also show the staff member around, go to lunch with him or her the first few days, explain more about how things get done, and help answer all the questions new staff members usually have.

Doctors are also responsible for making performance expectations clear. Frequent supportive performance reviews should occur as part of an ongoing orientation. The traditional six-month or twelve-month performance evaluation for staff members who have been in the practice for more than a year does not provide enough feedback for a new staff member who needs more frequent re-enforcement, direction, and encouragement. While the new staff member is in the initial stage of employment is the time for the doctor to give regular feedback as tasks are completed, along with specific suggestions for improvement, if necessary.

Do not assume that because a staff member has a solid work record or prior experience no guidance or direction is needed. The time spent with new employees also provides them with support and lifts their self-esteem as they are finding their place on your team. Make sure they are settling in, answer their questions, and review their responsibilities and training schedule. In meetings, let them know you're behind them right from the start. Time with the new staff member should be scheduled daily for the first week, then once at the end of the second, third, and fourth weeks. Make sure the new person understands your expectations and has a plan in place for meeting those goals. At the end of the first three months, schedule a performance planning and review session to evaluate new staff members' overall performance and to arrange any additional training.

Teach new staff members as much as possible about your practice and encourage them to learn. Be available and approachable. You must take the time to listen to your staff. Encourage them to use you as their sounding board. Although the problem may seem trite or small, it's probably extremely important to them. Listening is motivating. Unmotivated staff are certainly not happy and will begin to think they are in a position where they are unappreciated.

To sort out these feelings, listen to discover the strengths of your new staff members. Watch and look for tasks that they enjoy. When you see them do something well, let them do more of it. Then as their confidence builds, introduce them to more challenging and different situations. Help them to see the tangible results of their work. Believe it or not, staff welcome the chance to learn new skills on the job. Give them creative challenges and opportunities to collect proof of their value to the practice.

As staff members are urged to take more responsibility for managing their careers and because they face the prospect of numerous job changes, it follows that they should assume more responsibility for their orientation. New staff members are likely to be entering a practice today that will place a premium on soft skills, flexibility, and an ability to think and solve problems. In an evolving work world, experience alone is no longer sufficient for authority and high productivity. The ability to innovate and to learn is increasingly at a premium as practices seek staff members who are free of preconceptions and able to provide fresh ideas. Things are changing so rapidly that being well-schooled in a particular skill is not as important as before. Today, practices are looking for a fresh point of view without the baggage of the old way of doing things. More often we see that staff members who develop "soft" skills, such as communications skills, often rise to the top. Those with only "hard" technical skills fall behind. A staff member may have every technical skill out there, but without the soft skills to communicate ideas and information, a career path in dentistry will be limited. While doctors should supply direction and provide support, staff members need to learn these essential skills to ensure a more rapid and successful adjustment to their new position.

If you are wondering what types of skills will be needed, the U.S. Department of Labor and the American Society for Training and Development recently conducted a joint project to define what skills would be needed by professionals in the future. Not only did they indicate a need for individuals with a basic education, relationship skills, and the ability to self-manage, but also for people who could be trained, adaptability, and group effectiveness. Specifically, the skills needed for the practice of the future include people skills, communication, problem-solving, ability to change and be flexible, computer literacy, and creativity.

An orientation for new staff members as they begin working in your office provides them with the "safe place" necessary for everyone to feel comfortable communicating with each other. It's well known that high levels of communication cut the tension and awkwardness people often feel when they find themselves in new surroundings. Less stress and better communication promote teamwork and the spirit of cooperation necessary to ensure you start the new staff member off on the right foot!

Training Schedule for Business Office Personnel

Orientation:
1. Complete employment forms; complete new employee checklist.
2. Learn job description.
3. Review training schedule.
4. Review OSHA/HIPPA guidelines.
5. Meet individually with each staff member.

Week One:
1. Read the staff policy manual. Discuss questions with the doctor.
2. Learn names of all other staff members.
3. Observe and learn
   a. Patient flow; patient reception and dismissal.
   b. Methods of communication with patients at the desk and on the telephone.
   c. Handling of incoming telephone calls for the doctor and other staff members.
   d. Filing system.
   e. Supplies and forms storage and inventory system.
   f. Division and overlap of duties between business office personnel.
   g. What office coordinator and the doctor expect.

During weeks two and three, concentrate on those areas which will be within your job description.

Week Two:
1. Reinforce items from week one.
2. Learn methods of scheduling.
3. Learn to handle financial arrangements.
4. Learn recall system.
5. Begin to learn to use the computer for data entry and insurance billing.
6. Learn to check patients in and out.
7. Begin to learn charting method.
8. Learn to prepare for the "next day."

Week Three:
1. Reinforce items from weeks one and two.
2. Learn to post payments on the computer or peg board and ledger cards.
3. Learn to close computer for end-of-day reports or balance day sheet.
4. Learn to make bank deposits.
5. Learn processing of accounts payable.
6. Learn office terminology and dental vocabulary.

Week Four:
1. Reinforce items from weeks one, two, and three.
2. Learn insurance and Medicaid procedures.
3. Begin scheduling patients in appointment book.
4. Learn method of billing and aging of accounts for accounts receivable control.
5. Learn names of support personnel such as laboratory technician, accountant, lawyer, janitor, sales representatives.
6. Learn about correspondence needs of the doctor and the office in general.
7. Learn about statistics kept by the practice.

Week Five:
1. Reinforce items from weeks one, two, three, and four.
2. Become proficient in CPR. Enroll in a class if training is needed.
3. Meet with office coordinator and the doctor to review training process.
4. Learn office emergency procedures.

Training Schedule for Clinical Personnel

Orientation:
1. Complete employment forms; complete new employee checklist.
2. Learn job description.
3. Review training schedule.
4. Review OSHA/HIPPA guidelines.
5. Meet individually with each staff member.

Week One:
1. Read the staff policy manual. Discuss questions with the doctor.
2. Learn names of all other staff members.
3. Observe and learn
   a. Patient flow.
   b. Methods of communication with patients at the desk and on the telephone.
   c. How to greet and seat patients.
4. Learn different staff responsibilities.
5. Learn instrument and bur names.
6. Learn safety procedures for office.
7. Learn sterilization techniques.
8. Learn opening/closing duties.

Week Two:
1. Reinforce items from week one.
2. Learn tray set-ups.
3. Do some chair-side assisting with the hygienist under her direction.
4. Learn fee schedule and completion of super bill/routing slips.
5. Learn and practice rubber dam placement.
6. Review equipment maintenance schedule.
7. Learn office terminology and dental vocabulary.

Week Three:

1. Reinforce items from weeks one and two.
2. Learn charting methods.
3. Learn supply storage and inventory system.
4. Practice radiography techniques if you are certified. If not certified, enroll in a certification course as soon as possible.
5. Learn treatment procedures.
6. Do some chair-side assisting with the doctor under his/her direction.

Week Four:

1. Reinforce items from weeks one, two and three.
2. Learn scheduling methods.
3. Learn appliance names and uses.
4. Learn procedure for lab ordering and prescription completion.
5. Learn to stock chair-side units.
6. Learn to break down and clean x-ray processor and to replenish fluids.
7. Learn details of cleaning units, suctions, hand pieces, and other essential tools.

Week Five:

1. Reinforce items from weeks one, two, three and four.
2. Practice more chair-side assisting. Become proficient in techniques allowable under state law.
3. Learn procedure for handling medically compromised patients and their charts.
4. Learn to review health history forms and emergency-patient questions.
5. Learn office emergency procedure.
6. Become proficient in CPR. Enroll in a class if training is needed.

New Employee ( ) Checklist

Employee's Name:_____ Hire Date:_____

Date Completed:_____ By:_____

- ☐ Signed Resume and/or Employment Application on file.
- ☐ Personal information (birth date, phone numbers, addresses, emergency information) on file.
- ☐ W-4 forms completed.
- ☐ State and local tax withholding forms completed, if applicable.
- ☐ Report of new employees, filed with Department of Labor, if required by your state.
- ☐ Insurance application forms completed and benefit pamphlet distributed for each plan.
- ☐ Process for taking any immunizations, such as hepatitis vaccine, is discussed, if applicable.
- ☐ Orientation to infection control program discussed, including all policies, procedures and protective attire.
- ☐ Privacy practices reviewed.
- ☐ Systems/training manuals reviewed.
- ☐ Information regarding blood borne diseases discussed, if applicable.
- ☐ Work permit on file, if applicable.
- ☐ Verification of licenses and certifications, if applicable (copies of licenses and certifications in file).
- ☐ Hours/Work schedule, pay rate, pay days, overtime, meal, and break periods explained.
- ☐ Location of time card, time clock, or time sheet explained.

- ☐ Attendance, including whom to notify (and when) in cases of absence and tardiness.

- ☐ Name badge ordered.

- ☐ Key to office given to employee. Alarm system explained.

- ☐ Instructions given on opening and locking the office.

- ☐ Opening/closing duties explained.

- ☐ Security precautions (e.g., who can be admitted to the office) and emergency policies explained.

- ☐ Office tour completed.

- ☐ Location of storage and policy regarding personal belongings explained.

- ☐ Personnel manual discussed with the employee. Dress/Appearance/Uniforms discussed.

- ☐ Benefits mentioned with the explanation that details will be provided when eligibility starts.

- ☐ Employee acknowledgment form completed, including the employee's signed statement that he/she has read and understands the personnel manual. Introductory employee information included if appropriate.

- ☐ Job description for new employee and organization chart explained.

- ☐ Date set for employee performance planning and review conference.

- ☐ Explanation to employee of name that doctor prefers staff to use when referring to or addressing the doctor in front of patients.

Sample New Hire Letter

Dear _____,

Welcome to our practice. We are excited to have you join our team and look forward to working with you.

Your full-time employment with us as a Dental Assistant will begin Monday, April 14, 20XX. Your starting salary will be $17.50 per hour. You will generally be working 7:30 a.m. to 5:00 p.m., Monday through Thursday. Fridays are reserved for necessary staff training and patients with special needs.

As we spoke of earlier, the first 90 days of your employment will be considered an introductory period, after which you will be considered a regular employee. This introductory period will be used to provide training in the following skills, which are necessary to complete your job responsibilities.

Specific training will be provided to teach
- fabrication of indirect provisionals
- utilization of the intra-oral camera
- use of office computer software for charting and scheduling
- utilization of digital radiography

This individualized training will be incorporated into your regular training schedule that will teach you the policies and procedures of our office.

You and I will meet periodically during your introductory period to monitor your training progress and to answer questions. As stated in our staff policy manual, plan for a formal review of your progress on Monday, July 14, 20XX and every six months afterward.

Salary Conferences to discuss your salary, again, according to our staff policy manual, will be scheduled annually on your employment anniversary date. Your next Salary Conference is scheduled for Wednesday, April 14, 20XX.

Upon the completion of your introductory period, you will be eligible for the following fringe benefits:

- Paid holidays as listed in our Staff Policy Manual
- Paid vacation determined by length of service and listed in our Staff Policy Manual
- Well days
- All dental services provided by this office without charge
- Paid continuing education

In future years you will be eligible for additional fringe benefits such as medical reimbursement and participation in our profit-sharing plan. These are all described in our Staff Policy Manual for you to review.

Your official uniform is surgical scrubs. The clinical staff will describe the color coordination as I could never figure it out and just wear the same color every day.

Once again let me convey how happy I am to have you join our staff. It is my intention to make your time here productive and professionally rewarding. Although we will meet at regular intervals, please don't think twice about stopping to ask me a question.

Welcome aboard!

Bibliography

Conger, Sherry L. *How to Hire & Keep a Winning Team*. Phoenix, AZ: SmartPractice, 1991.

Ericksen, Bent. *Bent on Personnel*. Eugene, OR: Bent Ericksen Associates, 2003.

Flaherty, James. *Coaching: Evoking Excellence in Others*. Boston, MA: Butterworth-Heinemann, 1999.

Freeman, Marsha. *Standard Operating Procedures for Dentists*. Santa Maria, CA: Dental Communication Unlimited, 1997.

Massotto, Mike. *The 25 Surefire Ways to Destroy Your Dental Practice*. New York, NY: RJ Communications, LLC 2003.

Tracy, Brian. *Hire and Keep the Best People*. San Francisco, CA: Berrett-Koehler Publishers, Inc. 2001.

Tulgan, Bruce. *Managing Generation X*. Santa Monica, CA: Merritt Publishing, 1995.

Walton, Mary. *The Deming Management Method*. New York, NY: Putnam Publishing, 1986.

ABOUT LARRY M. GUZZARDO

*L*arry began his 24-year career as a training specialist, delivering in-house training programs such as active listening, customer service, stress management, and career development. Since turning to full-time dental consulting 14 years ago, Larry has focused his talents and experience exclusively on dental practice management, business systems, and leadership development. Larry has presented numerous workshop series including, "Winning Patient Acceptance," "Business Communication Systems," and "The Leadership Challenge." Larry has spoken to professionals across the United States on practice management, having received the Speaker's Appreciation Award from the Atlanta Dental Hygienist Association, Florida National Dental Congress, the New York Dental Society—Erie Canal Dental Conference, the Berkshire District Dental Association, and the National University of Mexico, as well as a Certificate of Appreciation from the Georgia Dental Association and has earned Certificates of Recognition from the American Dental Association. The Hinman Dental Society has presented Larry with Certificates of Appreciation for his table clinic presentations. He served as a member of the faculty at the Dawson Center for Advanced Dental Study where he taught patient communication. Larry is listed in the American Dental Society (ADA) Directory of Dental Practice Management Consultants. He is also certified to administer the DiSC Personality Profile, a member of the Academy of Dental Management Consultants, a Certified Standard Operating Procedures (SOP's) Consultant and has contributed articles for various publications.

Contact information:
Larry M. Guzzardo
P.O. Box 421635
Atlanta, GA 30342
Phone: (404) 252-5664
Fax: (404) 252-9157
Email: LMGuzzardo@aol.com

BROKEN APPOINTMENTS:
Practical Tips to Decrease Lost Time, The Steps to Gaining Control

by Cindy J. Ishimoto, CDPMA

P ractices must look to their system of appointment management before pointing the finger of blame and responsibility at the patient for canceling, failing to keep, or changing an appointment. Your system can either set the patient up for failure or guide them to success. Patients have many reasons for changing their appointments; certainly many are legitimate and we should be empathetic.

Lost time in a dental office can be the anchor that holds practices back from achieving their goals. Lost time hurts three people: the practice because it loses productivity, the patient who does not receive necessary care that helps them to experience a healthier beautiful smile, and the patient who couldn't have this appointment because it was previously reserved.

Practices must develop their communication system to a level of eloquence and elegance to assist the patients in learning the value of keeping their appointments.

There are many processes, linked together like a chain, that assist your practice in keeping the broken appointments and lost patient hours to a minimum. Your system will be only as strong as the weakest link in your chain. Staff development plays an integral part in the success of this system. Investing time to improve your communications will certainly strengthen that part of your system. The goal of all communications is to begin to have adult-to-adult communications instead of adult-to-child. Keep in mind that your goal is to coach your patients to learn new skills; you do that by helping them to accept responsibility for their appointments.

The first link of the chain in the broken appointment system to evaluate is your written or paper communications. The written word is not as effective as the spoken word; it is our voice that continues once the patient leaves the office.

There are three key areas to evaluate:

Appointment Cards

Typically, practices purchase their appointment cards with statements printed on them like: *If unable to keep this appointment kindly give us 24-hour notice.* Is this what you really mean? Most practices find it difficult if not impossible to fill openings that occur at the last minute. Have your appointment cards printed with: *This time has been reserved exclusively for you. Consider this card a confirmation of your appointment.* No options to cancel, or hints that it is okay if they do want to cancel. The responsibility for their appointment rests in the patients' hands where it belongs: a clearly stated written communication.

Review your appointment cards for clarity

Why not print your appointment card on the back of your business cards? This gives the appointment card a very professional and finished look. Also I recommend that you have only one or two lines for appointments. Having several lines to write out several appointments plants a seed for the patient to call and say, *I can't come this week; I'll just come to my next appointment.* I know that you may want to reserve multiple appointments but do not tell the patients that you have. Mark it in your system as a hold only, and when you inform the patient of the appointment, remove the hold from your system.

The appointment card is most clearly communicated if you have lines to write on. You will make fewer mistakes by writing out the appointment: e.g., Tuesday, April 6, 10:00, 2 hours. I like to recommend including the length of appointment time on the card so the patients know exactly how much time they will be spending with you at their next visit. Patients need to reserve their own schedules for the total time, not just what they think you said!

Brochure—Welcome Packet

Are you threatening your patients by including a cancellation policy in either your brochure or your welcome packet? Are you telling them that you charge them when they cancel or no-show? These are adult-to-child communications that actually communicate, *if you do this I'm going to get even with you and do that!*

Whatever you focus on is what you will create. Why not focus on language that is adult-to-adult, helping them to understand that appointments are valuable?

We have convenient office hours to serve our patients and we reserve appointment time exclusively for each patient. We will work with you to schedule appointments that maximize your care in the shortest number of appointments.

When we reserve an appointment for a patient, that patient is the only one scheduled at that time. The focus of the doctor and the hygienist is only on that patient's care and the time allowed is very important. Each appointment in a patient's treatment schedule moves that person closer to completing his or her needed dentistry.

Continuing Care Confirmation Cards

The word check-up needs to be eliminated from your verbal and written communications. It is a word of insignificance and unimportance: "Well it's just a check-up; it's no big deal if I don't go." Change it to continuing care, follow-up care, preventive care or recare. I recommend your cards say: *This is to verify the appointment you made with our hygienist for your preventive maintenance therapy, which includes an oral cancer screening, professional dental cleaning, necessary x-rays and a complete oral health examination.*

Another phrase that needs to be eliminated on your cards is: *If this time is not convenient please call for another appointment.* Why would you want to invite cancellations? This statement says, "We run our dental office for your convenience, and if anything comes along that is more important, call us and change your appointment; this appointment is no big deal and is not important." Consider including statements on your confirmation cards like: *This time has been reserved exclusively for you. We trust that no change in this appointment will be necessary. Consider this card a confirmation of your appointment. We look forward to seeing you on Tuesday, March 20th at 3:00 for 1 hour.*

The next link for your practice to strengthen is to put into place standard operating procedural guidelines in writing to handle the cancellations and failures. The first question you must answer is: Will you be charging or not? Since my recommendation for the written word was to be positive and non-threatening, it would be incongruent of me to recommend charging for broken appointments. I have seen this cause more damage than fixing the problem. Charging is like placing a band-aid on a gushing artery. Why not fix the system instead of attempting to stop the bleeding?

I would like to recommend a solid system that your practice can follow. At some point you really need to decide that the patients who continually cancel and fail don't really want to be in your practice. Make the decision to help them to be in another practice that will be happy to treat them under the limitations they place on themselves. I am including samples of letters that I would recommend you use as a starting point for the development of your own letters that match the style of your practice and the area that you are in.

After the first incident, no matter if it is a failure or a last-minute (less than 48-hour) notice, you should send the first letter:

We missed you and were worried about you. Unfortunately, this means your necessary treatment has been delayed. I'm sure you understand that when you miss appointment time reserved specifically for you, other patients in need of treatment cannot be seen. We really count on you being here at your scheduled time. In the future, we must ask that you give us 72 hours notice if you cannot keep your scheduled appointment. This courtesy will allow us to schedule other patients who are waiting for necessary treatment. I'm sure you understand that we must have policies along these lines. It is our policy to charge any patient for a broken appointment. However, since this is the first time this has happened, no charge is being made.

The last-minute change of appointment letter is similar:

I am sure your reason for cancelling your appointment with us was very important. We always try to understand conflicts and work with patients' schedules. When we schedule an appointment for a patient in this office, that patient is the only one scheduled at that time. Doctor's focus is only on that patient's care and the time allowed is very important. Each appointment in a treatment schedule moves the patient closer to completing the dentistry he or she agreed to have done. Cancelling appointments delays your necessary treatment.

I am sure you understand that we must have guidelines regarding cancellations. Our policy is that all appointment changes must be made 72 hours in advance, to allow us time to schedule other patients who are waiting for necessary treatment. Without this notice, we do charge for last-minute cancellations. However, since this is your first time, no charge is being made.

We hope in the future that you will give us the notice that allows us flexibility. More importantly, we hope you can keep your scheduled appointments so that together we can complete your necessary dentistry. I look forward to seeing you at your next appointment.

The second option is *I am sure your reasons for not keeping your reserved appointments with us were very important. We always try to understand conflicts and work with patients' schedules.*

When we schedule an appointment for a patient in this office, that patient is the only one scheduled at that time. The focus of the doctor and the hygienist is only on that patient's care and the time allowed is very important. Each appointment in a treatment schedule moves the patient closer to completing the dentistry he or she agreed to have done. Cancelling appointments delays your necessary treatment. As you know, early diagnosis of developing problems that may not be visible to you can also save you from added pain and expense. If your teeth seem healthy, keep in mind that when they hurt the damage has already occurred. The investment in prevention is less than the expense of emergency dental care.

Reserved appointment time is for patients who are committed to completing their necessary dentistry. We are placing you on our priority call list and will call you to schedule an appointment when a change in our schedule occurs. If these changes occur, they will be either the day before or the day of the available time.

I'm sure you understand that when you miss appointment time reserved specifically for you, other patients in need of treatment cannot be seen. We have elected to have policies in place in order to serve patients at the level of their respect for our reserved times.

We will call you when time is available so we can work together to complete your necessary dentistry and help you to enjoy a higher level of dental health.

I recommend that the doctor sign the letters because there is so much more importance placed on it when the patient sees the doctor's signature. They will do anything to keep from having the doctor be angry with them. Most patients aren't even aware that the doctor knows when they miss their appointments! Anonymity for the patients is such a safe place: when you are exposed, it truly becomes uncomfortable and not so easy to cancel again. It's like cutting school: the first time you get caught makes you less likely to do it again.

The following is a template to assist you in developing your own broken appointment system guidelines.

- After the 1st cancellation or no show: send the kinder, gentler letter.
- After the 2nd cancellation or no show: place the patient on the priority call list.
- After the 3rd cancellation or no show: the team needs to discuss how they will deal with this patient. Your option may be to place him or her on the call list permanently. Or you may release the patient so he or she may go to a practice that is willing to treat the patient under the limitations they place on themselves.

Now that you have looked at your written communications and strengthened those links, it is important to work on the spoken word.

So many times in dental practices I hear the team say, *we have so much lost time—what are those business people doing—why can't they stop it or prevent it, don't they know how important it is to keep all of us scheduled?* The misconception is that it is a business staff problem. Actually, the entire team is responsible for preventing broken appointments.

High-Impact Link 1

If the appointment does not appear to be important to the office, how can you expect it to be other than unimportant to the patient? The key here is placing value for every appointment, every patient. If patients understand why they need treatment, they will be committed to the process of coming for their appointments.

Rule for Doctors, Hygienists, and Assistants: Never let the patient out of the chair without thirty seconds of eye-to-eye contact and a heart-to-heart talk.

Example: "At your next appointment we will be doing your crown on the upper left, that's the one with the really large old filling that is breaking apart. It is very important that you keep the appointment so together we can take care of that problem."

I recommend that the doctor say this because the patients respect what the doctor has to say and place more value on appointments if the doctor explains to them why.

Example for Hygienists: "Steve, things are looking much better and we are seeing improvement. However, I'm still concerned about that lower left area where your bridge is. I'm going to be evaluating that area at your 6-month continuing care appointment, so it will be important for you to keep your appointment."

Example for hygienists for a patient with good oral hygiene: "John, at your next continuing care appointment we'll be providing your oral cancer screening and thorough preventive therapy. It's important that you keep your appointment because together we have been helping you to maintain a stable level of health and we want to continue on that same positive path."

Remember that if you say it, you need to write it down. Your area of concern for this patient should be noted in your appointment system and your chart notes. If you have the ability to print this note on the pre-confirmation card and personalize the card, it will have its greatest impact.

High-Impact Link 2

When confirming continuing care appointments, I recommend you say, *"Steve, this is Diane from Dr. Jones' office. Chris, our hygienist, asked me to call and verify your appointment for cleaning, oral cancer screening, and checking that lower left area she mentioned to you."*

Patients won't buy the solution to their problem until they buy the fact that there is a problem. The solution is, of course, their appointment. The problem is what you informed them your concern is. If they agree there is a concern or a problem, they will keep their appointment, which solves the problem!

Being liked by our patients is something we all want. Saying things to please them, such as, "You are doing a great job and you just need a cleaning," sounds great but it causes appointment failures. Patients will like you more if you tell the truth and help them to understand the importance of keeping their appointments.

When dismissing the patients at the business office, it is important that you inform the business staff of the reason this patient needs to keep the next appointment. If you are scheduling in the treatment area, put the reason in the appointment notes. As you present the appointment card to the patient, state the reason he needs to return again, the appointment date, time, and length, and that you look forward to seeing him.

What is your confirmation policy? Do you confirm every single appointment? If so, you will have the same rate of appointment failures as those who don't confirm any appointments. If you confirm all of your patients, they are expecting your call. If you don't reach them, there is an 80 percent chance that they will no-show their appointment. They always say, *"But you didn't remind me."*

One third of your patients are annoyed by the phone calls. They are responsible people who always keep their appointments. You don't even finish your confirmation statement before they say, "I know!" The second third of your patients appreciate your call, thank-you for the call, and wouldn't keep the appointment without the call. The final third are too lazy to look up your phone number, dial the phone, and change their appointment. They wait until you call to confirm and they say, *"I was just getting ready to call."*

Do not make an abrupt change to not confirming your patient's appointments unless you want to double, maybe triple, your lost time. Take the middle of the road for success. Hand the appointment card to your patients and say, *"Mrs. Jones, this card is a confirmation of your appointment. Most of our patients find that this is enough for them. Will this work for you? Or if you like, I will be more than happy to call you 48 hours prior to your appointment."*

Many patients will say, *"No problem, I've never missed an appointment. I will mark my calendar."* Respond by saying, *"Great, I'll make a note in our appointment system indicating that you will be responsible for your reserved time."* If they request a phone call, tell them that it is your pleasure to make the call and that you are placing a note in the appointment system so that everyone knows the patient requested phone verification. If you will do this you should be able to reduce the number of confirmation calls by at least one-third to one-half.

If you pre-appoint hygiene, you need to send out pre-confirmation cards three weeks prior to the appointment and do telephone verification two days prior to the appointment. Calling the day before only causes stress. You won't allow them to change within 24 hours, so why are you confirming at that time?

Unmotivated Staff

If the team feels that they are going to make the same pay for the same number of hours worked no matter how many patients cancel, they will let the patients cancel. It will be less hectic for them and they can use the time to catch up on paperwork.

If you are understaffed and the team has too much work to do and not enough time to complete all of the tasks, they will be looking for lost time to get caught up. Non-patient time is their chance to do that. Allowing patients to cancel, or not filling open time is not done consciously, it is done out of frustration to find time to complete the tasks

Monitoring lost time is important for each practice to do. You need to have an accurate picture of your hourly production. If you don't subtract the lost time you really don't know what your hourly production is. Raises for certain team members should be based on productivity, and if lost time impacts whether or not they will receive a raise they need to be told. Share with them how many hours were lost, what it cost the practice in production, and what impact it had on the overhead. This lost time information and how it impacts each staff member can be a way to help motivate them to keep the appointment times filled with patients who need treatment.

Doctor lost time should be no more than 3-4 hours per month, and hygiene lost time should be no more than 4-5 hours per month. This does not mean per hygienist. If you have two full time hygienists you should have no more than 6-8 lost hours per month. Keep in mind eight hours of time is one full day of hygiene lost. You can create a bonus system to reward the decrease in lost hours.

Remember that lost time impacts everyone: the patients who are waiting for appointments don't get served, the overhead keeps on going with no income to decrease it, the opportunity to serve more patients is lost, and time, the most precious practice commodity, is wasted.

Weak Verbal Skills

The number one cause for broken appointments is weak verbal skills on the part of the doctor and the team.

Example: *"I don't have an opening that day and time so let me put you on our cancellation list. We get 5-6 cancellations in a day. I'm sure we can get you in sooner."*

You just told your patients that your biggest problem in this practice is cancellations and that it is okay to cancel. We even have a list of people to fill in appointments, so it is no problem to cancel. Eliminate the word "cancel" from your vocabulary and use "change of schedule" instead!

Verbal Skills to Use

When you call a patient to fill in a change of schedule, say, *"Mr. Woods, this is Cindy from Dr. Jones' office. We have had a change in doctor's schedule tomorrow and I immediately thought of you. Would you like to come in tomorrow for that really important crown prep instead of waiting until next week?"* Do not say; *"Would you like to come in tomorrow? Another patient just canceled her appointment."*

Which one sounds better? As the patient, I don't want to be made to feel like I am second best and that I get the left-over appointments. Patients want to feel hand-picked and important, so help them to feel that way by choosing empowering language.

Telephone confirmation conversation:

"Good afternoon Mrs. _____ this is _____ from Dr. _____'s office. Dr. asked me to call and let you know he is expecting you on (Day & date) at (time) for (length of appointment) We will be doing your (type of treatment) in the upper right. Do you have any questions about your appointment? We're looking forward to serving you."

"Good afternoon Mrs. _____ this is _____ from Dr. _____'s office. Our hygienist Jane, asked me to call and let you know she is expecting you on (Day & date) at (time) for (length of appointment) She will be doing your (type of treatment), oral cancer screening and checking that (area of concern). Do you have any questions about your appointment? We're looking forward to serving you."

Quick-to-Solve Patient Problems

One of the toughest habits to break is politeness and kindness: the, "oh don't worry about inconveniencing us" attitude. We have to be ready to resolve whatever problem the patient has to a win-win conclusion: we keep the appointment time on our books and they get their needed dentistry completed.

What should you do if the patient calls and says, *"I've been sick for two days and I waited till now because I was hoping I would feel better. I'm sorry but I am too sick to come for my appointment."*

You can never accuse a patient of lying about illness. The best thing you can do is to purchase a box of get well cards, have everyone on the staff write a 4-5 word message to no one in particular, and sign the cards. Seal the cards and keep them at the scheduling coordinator's desk. When someone says he or she is sick, addressing the card to their place of work has the most impact. Sending the card to their home works well too; in both cases mail it the moment the appointment changes. Two things will happen. The person who is genuinely ill will appreciate your thoughtfulness: the other may have some explaining to do to a spouse, co-worker, or boss.

How about the old stand by of, *"My car broke down and I don't have a way in to the office."* Keep in mind that people find transportation to places they really want to go. You need to give permission to your team to send and pay for a taxi for long appointments. Your response should be, *"Mrs. Patient, what time would you like a taxi? We will be happy to arrange that for you if need be."* The patient may say excuse me or what did you say and then your response should be, *"As you know I reserved doctor's entire mid-morning just for you. I would rather send a taxi at office expense than to go back and tell doctor he will be just sitting around for two hours. It will be difficult if not impossible to fill this time at such short notice."* Most patients say they didn't realize how important it was and will work out their transportation problems and get to their appointment. Some don't and you may have to send a taxi.

Things to Keep In Mind

- Doctors need to give their team permission to make the patients feel slightly guilty, so that they can be firm and friendly in order to decrease the number of broken appointments.
- The tone of voice of the scheduling coordinator can either encourage or discourage broken appointments. Do you make it easy for the patient to cancel or do you have firm and friendly persuasive techniques to help them keep the appointment?
- Remember the standing rule is: A good scheduling coordinator does not leave today until tomorrow's holes in the schedule are filled. I know at 4:00 p.m. you could learn to hate this rule.
- A good scheduling coordinator can talk 65-70 percent of the

patients into keeping their appointments. You should track this and report your success at your staff meetings.

- When a patient calls last minute with "something came up," do not go to the trouble of rescheduling that inconsiderate patient now! Say, *"Mrs. Patient, I need to be calling patients on my priority call appointment list to try and fill this appointment time. We have patients needing dentistry that want to see the doctor/hygienist. I'll be in touch with you. Bye."*
- Remember the goal is to always be polite and to inform patients that we don't appreciate failed appointments, last minute cancellations or feeble excuses. Re-training your patients takes time. Invest in this and it will pay off in the long run.
- Evaluate each part of the system to improve, enhance or change your practice's weak links. If you will make the changes to a more effective presentation, you will begin to experience a decrease in lost time.

ABOUT CINDY J. ISHIMOTO, CDPMA

*C*indy Ishimoto began her career in dentistry over 30 years ago as a dental assistant and business auxiliary. She then went on to a management position and has successfully consulted practices for over 25 years. She is well-known for her expertise in the business and financial management of the practice and her team-building skills. Cindy is also a well-known lecturer and author. She has presented programs at major meetings, state meetings, and conferences and also self sponsors many seminars. She is a member of the National Speakers Association. Consulting is Cindy's passion, teaching practices processes that help them clearly define their needs, wants, and dreams. She helps them establish systems that balance serving patients, profitability, and enjoyment of profession. Her goal is to help each practice she works with to experience well-being and financial success. Cindy's consulting philosophy was a match with Jameson Management and she was selected to be a member of their consulting team. Cindy continues to broaden her scope of consulting across the United States, United Kingdom, and beyond.

Contact information:
Cindy Ishimoto
314 Ekoa Place
Wailuku, HI 96793
Phone: (808) 244-7344
Email: CIshimoto@aol.com
Website: www.cindyishimoto.com

"IT COSTS TOO MUCH":
Maximizing a Healthcare Financing Program

by Cathy Jameson

A ccording to the most recent surveys by the American Dental Association, the number one reason that people do not go to the dentist is that "it costs too much." If a person comes to a dental practice, they either need or want something—or they probably wouldn't come. So, if someone walks out the door not saying "yes'" to treatment, there is a reason. And the major reason is cost.

Here is the challenge: to find ways for patients to receive the care that they want to receive—and that the dentist wants to provide—by finding solutions to patients' financial challenges. And, at the same time, it is important to maintain a stable financial environment for the practice. So, how does one marry these two issues: by increasing case acceptance while staying out of the banking business. One important way is to become involved with and to maximize a healthcare financing program.

Six Ways To Maximize A Healthcare Financing Program

Many dental professionals believe in the concept of patient financing but are frustrated because they can't seem to get the patients interested, or they bump into objections that seem to close the door on this financial option. So, they put the materials in the drawer and say, "Oh, that didn't work for us." The programs will work if worked properly. And if worked properly, the benefits to the patient and the practice are measurable. For example, determine the value of the average treatment plan in the practice. If one more person per week proceeds with treatment because he can now afford it, what would that mean? Take this average treatment plan fee, multiply that by 4 weeks in the month and that by 12 months in the year. For example, if one person per week goes ahead with $500 worth of treatment, let's see what that looks like.

$500 per week x 4 weeks in the month = $2000 per month
x 12 = $24,000 per year

And so on. Do the math. What would this mean to the practice?

Or, could it be possible that one person a day might be able to proceed with $500 worth of treatment if she had a convenient way to pay?

$500 per day x 200 days per year (average in the country)
= $100,000 per year of additional revenue

This could occur if one person per day goes ahead with a minimal amount of treatment because patients can spread out the payments and not have to come up with a large amount at one time. (And I am talking about $500—not $5,000) Give the following six ideas a try. They work!

1. Introduce the Program to the Entire Patient Family

In a special mailing, or in a regularly published patient education newsletter, tell the existing patient family about the financing program. Present the program in an exciting, informative manner—one that stresses the benefits to the patient. Point out how the program will benefit the patient and/or the patient's family. Do not stress how much it will benefit the practice.

In this special mailing include a brochure about the program—some offices include an application. Make it easy for the patient to become involved. Eliminate as many barriers as possible.

Some patients will not need the program. If they don't need financial assistance, they won't apply. However, some people may not be coming to the practice on a regular basis or may be putting off needed or desired treatment because of cost. Others may have completed one phase of treatment but do not schedule the next phase because of money. If this is the case, establishing a line of credit may break the cost barrier. If they owe the financing program instead of the practice, they may be more willing and able to go ahead with treatment. Plus, the monthly payments will, more than likely, be smaller.

Practices spend a great deal of time nurturing a new patient flow. That's essential. However, nurturing the existing patient family makes good sense as well. Most practices can double from within by nurturing that which they already have—their own patient family.

Remember that repetition is the key to learning and the key to getting good results from marketing efforts. Do not introduce a financial policy or a healthcare financing program once and expect it to be readily accepted. It won't be. The program must be repetitively reintroduced via newsletters, mailings, telephone ads, newspaper articles, verbal introduction during the financial presentation, and continuous, positive conversations about this option.

2. Accounts Receivable Transfer

Every day that an account sits on the books doing nothing, money is lost because of (1) the cost of running a banking business, (2) the chances of never collecting the account, and (3) the loss of the dollar as it depreciates in value. These factors make the carrying of accounts a difficult business process.

Therefore, if the practice has existing accounts receivable, consider making an active effort to transfer as many of those accounts as possible to a healthcare financing program. Get the money in the bank and let professionals take over the management of these accounts.

Suggested steps for this transfer:
1. Analyze your accounts receivable. Determine the following:
   a. How much is insurance? How much is private pay?
   b. Of the private pay accounts, how many are 30, 60, 90, (or more) days past due?
   c. Those accounts that are extremely past due and have had no activity may need to be turned over for legal action. (Make sure that the dentist approves all accounts to be turned over or written off.) Be certain that a concerted effort to collect the account has been made, and that the patient has been

unwilling to negotiate a settlement before an account is turned over for collection.

2. For all of the remaining accounts, create a letter introducing the idea of transferring accounts to the healthcare financing. Expound on the following benefits of the program, such as:

a. Longer time in which to pay the account.

b. Smaller monthly payments.

c. No large payments due at one time.

d. No initial or yearly fee to become involved with the program.

e. Available credit for emergencies or for necessary and desired treatment.

f. If you are charging a service fee that is higher than the financing program, stress the benefit of the lower service fee. (Make sure it is.)

3. Send an application and a brochure with this letter. Send this letter in a separate mailing, not with statements. Print the letter on letterhead stationery and place it in a letterhead envelope. This needs to be a special mailing so that it receives special attention.

Once the first mailing has been sent, begin a telephone campaign to all of those patients who do not respond. Track these telephone calls. Make notes of who has been called, those who were sent an application, the date the application was sent, the date it was received back in the office, and any comments related to the conversation.

Please note that the sooner someone is contacted about a past due account, the better. Any contact with a patient with a past due account is a good time to encourage him to work with you to transfer the balance. The best way to collect is face to face. The second best way is over the phone. The third best way is through the written word.

At the next statement run—another month has passed—send a follow-up letter with another brochure and another application to anyone who has not yet transferred the account.

In this letter, let patients know that there has been a change in the accounting methods of the practice and that a financial service is now being offered to those who wish to extend their payments over a long period of time. Once again, stress the benefits of the program and the benefits to the individuals. Continue the telephone campaign.

4. By now, there should have been a strong response to the transfer process—especially if the recommended regime has been followed carefully and with commitment. If there is not going to be a commitment to follow the campaign through to the end—with consistency—don't expect a great response.

5. Continue the telephone campaign until a negotiated settlement of the account and/or a clear idea of how that account will be reconciled has been agreed upon.

If a patient is abiding by a previously agreed upon financial arrangement, go ahead and offer the new program to her, but willingly allow her to maintain the older agreement if it is comfortable.

Dental team members will love the accounts receivable transfer because they are going to get out of the statement and collection business and have more time to take care of other necessary duties within the practice, including taking care of patients. They want to spend their time nurturing relationships with patients, educating them about treatment needs and possibilities, and finding financial solutions for patients—rather than spending time sending statements, calling past due accounts, or calling insurance companies.

Patients will accept the accounts receivable transfer because most patients would rather owe a financing institution than owe the dentist. In addition, their payments will probably be less per month.

Take this protocol and individualize it to fit you. No two practices are alike, but these concepts will fit any practice. Fine tune the concepts to make them your own. Get that money into the bank account. That's where it needs to be.

3. Chart Auditing

Most dentists will agree that there is more dentistry sitting in their charts waiting to be done than they have ever done in their practicing days. We now know that the main reason that people do not proceed with dental care is the cost. Therefore, going through the charts of existing patients to reactivate these people into the practice or to reinforce the need for the dental treatment can be a super practice builder—especially when this effort is combined with the introduction of a healthcare financing program. Consider auditing all charts in a systematic manner, and auditing the charts on a daily basis.

The following lists suggest a procedure to follow in a full audit of charts.

- The team sets the goal of what they want to accomplish by performing the chart audit. They determine the end result they expect and intend to accomplish.
- The objectives and strategies are defined: What are they going to do? How are they going to do it? What resources might they need? What obstacles or barriers might get in the way and how can they overcome them?
- The person or persons responsible for each specific task are assigned their specifically detailed duties.
- The time frame is set. Time activate each step.
- Evaluate your progress and your success.

Information to be gathered on each patient:
- Date the person was called regarding existing treatment
- Person's name
- Telephone number
- Last date seen
- Details of any dentistry diagnosed but left incomplete
- If the patient has insurance or not
- Details about their policy
- If the patient is a part of the healthcare financing program at this time or not and/or how much their first monthly payment would be if they financed
- If the person is interested in the financing program, note the date the application was sent
- The date the application was returned
- Comments relative to care or expectations

It is best to audit a specific number of charts per week. Once the charts have been audited and the above mentioned information has been gathered, make the telephone calls. Once all those calls have been made and patients have been contacted, go on to the next set of charts. Some offices audit all the charts but never make the phone calls. That would be a waste of time—and no one has time to waste.

Once the data has been gathered for this week's charts, make courteous marketing telephone calls to those patients to (1) express concern about their care, (2) let them know they have not been forgotten, (3) reinforce the need for treatment, and (4) explain the new financing program.

Approach this effort steadily and with a positive attitude. Sixty-four percent of the people promoting a service or a product never ask a potential customer/client to proceed. Learn to ask! Ask patients to make a decision that is good for them—to get and maintain a healthy mouth, teeth, and gums for a lifetime.

Not everyone will respond by scheduling an appointment, but this is no reason for discouragement. If 20-30 percent of the people contacted schedule an appointment, this is good. Both the patient and the practice will be winners. Make sure that, as patients are contacted about necessary treatment, there is an introduction of the healthcare financing program. The following conversation is an example of how to proceed.

Business Administrator: *Ms. Jones? This is Cathy, from Dr. Jameson's office. How are you? Ms. Jones, Dr. Jameson has been reviewing your records and realized that the dental treatment that he had recommended for you has not been completed at this time, and he was concerned. You are missing a tooth on the lower left area of your mouth and the adjacent teeth are shifting, and both you and the doctor were concerned about the potential loss of more teeth. He asked that I call you to see if you had any questions about the treatment that he has prescribed.*

One of the reasons we're calling is to tell you about an exciting new program that we have available in our practice. Ms. Jones, we have become involved with a program that allows our patients to finance their dentistry and pay it out over a period of time with very small monthly payments. Ms. Jones, I see that you have dental insurance through XYZ company and that is great. Dental insurance has been so helpful to so many of our patients. It serves as a wonderful supplement to their healthcare budget. Our new program lets you finance your dental care including the balance that insurance does not cover.

In reviewing your record, I see that the fee for the treatment that Dr. Jameson is recommending for you is approximately $2,300. We estimate your insurance company will pay about $1,000. Therefore, we could file your insurance as a service to you and for about $35 per month you could finance your estimated portion. You could spread the payments out over a period of time, keep the payments small enough to be comfortable, not put yourself under any financial stress, and, best of all, you could proceed with the treatment that both you and the doctor believe is best for you. Would this be something of interest to you?

Patient: Yes, this sounds good to me. I have wanted to have this done, but there was no way I could afford it. I didn't have enough money. But I can pay $35 a month.

Business Administrator: Ms. Jones, let me gather some information from you right now. I will transmit this information to our financial partner and within a matter of minutes, we will know if they have been able to extend a line of credit to you. Once they have given us the go-ahead, we can schedule an appointment and begin your treatment. How does that sound?

If for some reason the patient wants to have information and an application sent in the mail, do so. However, be sure to track this mailing. Then, if an application has not been received back in the office, that is an alert. It is time to make a phone call to Ms. Jones.

Use of a tracking device provides notification as to when an application has left the office and when it is returned. Otherwise a lot of information could fall through the cracks. Track this chart audit and the mailing of any applications.

Daily chart audits through the daily meeting: There are many important parts to a productive daily meeting, but one of those parts is to identify dentistry that has been diagnosed but not completed. Most practices will find that 50–75 percent of patients coming to the office on any given day need some treatment beyond today—either with the hygienist or the dentist. Instead of spending a great deal of time during the daily meeting talking about what needs to be done that day, make note of what the patient needs next. Then, when the patient is in the treatment area, have a conversation about the next phase of necessary dentistry. Use the intra-oral or digital camera to highlight the next area of concern. Stress the benefits of proceeding with treatment and discuss any problems that may arise if the person doesn't proceed.

The goal is to have more people saying "yes" to the treatment that has been diagnosed but not provided. Get the dentistry out of the charts and into the mouths of the patients. The doctor would not diagnose and recommend treatment if the patient didn't need it. Therefore, the patient benefits when he/she is encouraged to proceed. By following this protocol regularly at the daily meeting, the entire team is sharing in the responsibility of doing ongoing chart audits.

4. Insurance

Many people put off their treatment in spite of the fact that they have dental insurance. Available benefits are not being used because of the inability to pay the estimated patient portion—or co-pay. On an ongoing basis, a practice needs to inform insured patients about the opportunity to utilize insurance benefits and to also have convenient monthly payments for the estimated patient portion. More patients will be able to use their insurance and may be able to proceed with treatment that they might otherwise put off.

If a practice is not taking insurance on assignment but patients are paying in full and being reimbursed by the insurance company directly, terrific. However, some people may choose to finance their entire treatment so that the monthly payments will be comfortable for them.

5. Continuous Care

Many people do not stay on a regular program of continuous care in hygiene or they do not involve all members of their family in your program because the investment is prohibitive. That's the last thing any dental professional wants—for patients to put off needed or desired care because of the cost.

Introducing the financing program to hygiene patients or through a hygiene retention program will not only allow more patients to receive this valuable service, but it will also help nurture this lifeblood of the practice, the hygiene department.

If a practice is involved with a nonsurgical periodontal program or is offering sealant therapy, many patients want and need this care but find the financial responsibility difficult. However, if they find that they can obtain these treatments and that the monthly investment will fit nicely into the family budget, many will proceed.

6. Case Presentation

At the time of the case presentation or consultation appointment, it is appropriate to introduce the financing program. Otherwise, as the doctor or treatment coordinator is trying to educate the patient about the services being recommended, the patient may be thinking of nothing but the cost. The human mind can think of only one thing at a time. Therefore, if a patient is calculating what the treatment may cost, he may not hear a word about the treatment. It is better to address a potential barrier before the patient brings it up. Timing is important.

Sometimes a patient starts asking about money before a discussion of the clinical dentistry has taken place. If a fee is quoted too early, that can be worse than not quoting a fee at all. If a fee is quoted—the discussion turns to money and the patient doesn't really know what he/she is buying. A person must see the value of the treatment (the end results and benefits) before a discussion of money takes place. For example, consider the following conversation.

Patient: *Before you even start, Doc, just get to the bottom line. How much is this going to be?*

Dr.: *Mr. Jones, sounds like you are concerned about the financing of your dental care.*

Patient: *You bet I am!*

Dr.: *I can certainly appreciate that. However, before we discuss your financial responsibility, let me tell you that we have convenient financial options right here in our practice. Before we proceed with treatment, we will make sure that you are comfortable with the financing of the treatment. But for right now, I would like to discuss the treatment*

I feel would be best for you. Let's focus on those recommendations, and then we will discuss the financing thoroughly. Is that okay with you?

Once the patient has agreed, proceed with the clinical presentation. Defuse the fear of cost. Then the patient will be able to focus his attention on the clinical presentation. He will appreciate the empathy expressed about his financial concerns, but the money questions will be put where they belong—and where they can be addressed most effectively.

Offer the best treatment possible, make the financing of the dentistry comfortable, and then get out of the way. Let the patient make the decision of whether or not to proceed.

Summary

Study these six methods for integrating a healthcare financing program. A strategic plan of action needs to be determined, written, and implemented.

By maximizing a healthcare financing program, the practice wins by running more efficiently and effectively. Patients win because they are able to have the care that they want and need. Dentists win because they are able to do the dentistry they love to do. Plus, they will be able to schedule longer appointments doing more dentistry per appointment, which is a productive, profitable, and stress-controlled way to practice.

ABOUT CATHY JAMESON

*C*athy Jameson is founder, president, and chief executive officer of Jameson Management, Inc., an international dental lecture and consulting firm. The Jameson Method of Management, developed by Cathy, helps dentists and their teams increase productivity and profitability and control stress by focusing on the 25 systems within a dental practice. She and her team of consultants have lectured and consulted in 19 countries and have offices in New York and the United Kingdom, in addition to their two Oklahoma offices. The Jameson Management team has changed thousands of lives through lectures and in-office consulting as well as books, CDs, DVDs and other products. The combined 468 years of experience in the dental field of Jameson consultants allows them to bring workable and effective strategies to dental teams every day worldwide.

Contact information:
Cathy Jameson
Jameson Management, Inc.
P.O. Box 488
Davis, OK 73003
Phone: (877) 369-5558
Email: info@jamesonmanagement.com
Website: www.jamesonmanagement.com

HAPPY EMPLOYEES = PRODUCTIVE PRACTICE

by Linda Miles, CSP, CMC

As a management consultant I'm frequently asked: "Where do I find exceptional employees?" I cannot find myself repeating enough: You don't find them, you create them. Having an office with a positive environment that brings out the best in all workers is the key. Some dentists have great skills in hiring and staff retention while others constantly struggle. One could say it's a gift, curse, or good versus bad luck, but ultimately it's a leadership and communication issue.

The Hiring Process

While ads are not the only way to attract likely candidates to fill an opening on the team, they are the avenue many dentists use to fill vacancies. Many ads are filled with scant abbreviations or make the job sound "cushy," invariably attracting the wrong type of employee. Brief ads come across to the potential applicant as: *"Don't go there, they are cheap."* However, ads that try to make the job appear to be the best thing since sliced bread usually attract those looking for a generous benefit package, four-day workweek, time off with pay, and bonuses.

Remember, there will always be two types of employees: Givers and Takers. The right ad always attracts Givers, the employees dentists need and want. Givers come to work with one thought in mind . . . What can I do for my patients, employer, and co-workers to make this day a little easier and more productive. Takers want to know what the practice can do for them and often state, *"That's not my job."*

Using words that describe the person you would enjoy having as part of the practice is a must. A sample introduction for any position might begin with questions such as, *"Are you enthusiastic, dependable, self-motivated and an excellent communicator,"* or, *"Are you dedicated, accountable, and a hard-working team player?"* Or the ad could begin with a statement: *"Seeking an exceptional person looking for a long-term career in dentistry, not a job."* Potential applicants will think *I wasn't really looking for a change of employment, but I think this ad just described me. Sounds like they need me.* If you really want to attract good prospects, always include the following sentence if it pertains to your practice: *"Would you like to work in a patient-centered practice that truly appreciates staff?"*

I've seen amazing figures concerning the number of good applicants who were interviewed when using these ads. One client recently had 23 resumes from a positively worded ad versus a typical ad. It's always beneficial to search for the right personal traits as clinical or business skills can be learned. (Note: Packets of sample ads, applications for employment, job descriptions, interviewing forms, performance evaluations and ideas for motivating the dental team are available on our website at www.DentalManagementU.com.)

Interviewing

Interviewing should be conducted soon after the applications and resumes are received because good people don't stay unemployed for very long. Procrastinating employers often lose good applicants. Get your pre-interviewing done quickly, and don't take forever to invite the applicants back for a second interview. Take ample time to thoroughly interview each of the top two or three candidates. I recommend the practice administrator and hygienist to do the pre-interviewing for another hygienist, the PA and clinical assistant for the next dental assistant, narrowing it down to the top three candidates for the dentist to do the final interviewing.

Soon after interviews are completed and the position has been filled, it is a courtesy gesture to send a thank-you note to all those interviewed in round one. It is also gracious to send a small floral arrangement to the top two or three who went through the final interview and possibly a half or full-day working interview. (Note: Do not pay for working interviews because by law, you just became their last employer.) Presenting a gift certificate is a much better idea than salary for the time of observation.

Having the team take the top two or three applicants out to lunch individually gives great insight into social skills and often inside information that is illegal to ask on an interview, such as marital status, spouse's job status, social likes and dislikes, number and ages of children, and plans for future additions to the family.

Unsolicited information is to be expected in social settings and can be of great value in narrowing the field to the ideal candidate. If the applicant spent the entire hour at lunch slandering his or her last employer, it is an indication you will the next one slandered. If the applicant talks about unhealthy habits, such as heavy partying or missing work, is rude to wait staff, or has difficulty communicating, surely this isn't the ideal candidate for the position.

The final interview process should be the DiSC Behavioral Profile or similar behavioral assessment. While this can't be used as the only final interview tool, it is good to know if and how the applicant will fit into the team you already possess. The perfect team behavioral profile ratios are 10-15 percent D's or C's, (D's are direct, decisive and strong leaders. C's are cautious, correct and perfectionists); 25 percent high I's = creative people, persons who love to talk but seem a bit disorganized. 50 percent are high S's = Steadfast, loyal, hard workers, but can sometimes be resistant to change.

Additional hiring suggestions: I recommend written employee performance reviews at 30 and 90 days for new hires and every year in the employee's anniversary month. The employer(s) should fill out the performance forms, along with the employee for self-evaluation, and anonymously by each co-worker, (averaged by the practice administrator) as the peer review evaluations. (Note: Employees will display the highest degree of teamwork and accountability three to four months before their peer review evaluations.) A sample employee evaluation is provided at the end of this chapter.

I also recommend that new employees be assigned a buddy their first two weeks on staff. This person acts as their contact for asking questions as complex as how to handle a clinical or business procedure or as simple as where to store personal belongings or how to turn on the microwave.

Experienced new employees are often reticent to offer fresh ideas or advice to coworkers for fear of others thinking harshly of them. Yet many new employees harbor a wealth of good information when asked. Supply new employees with a notepad to carry around the first three weeks, and let them know that if they have any suggestions to please make note of them. The facilitator for the next staff meeting will then ask them to share these ideas at the next staff meeting. New employees see things with fresh eyes, and encouraging their input can often produce beneficial advice.

Employee Motivation

Most dental employees are naturally born caretakers that thrive on appreciation. However, employers must learn how to get ordinary people to establish extraordinary levels of enthusiasm. REMEMBER: Hire . . . Train . . . Trust . . . Praise . . . (In that order) If an employee is not properly trained, he or she can't be fully trusted. Until there is trust, there is no loyalty. Additionally, if the employee is not fully trained she will never live up to the employer's expectations. Therefore, the dentist has little to praise. This is a vicious cycle which, unfortunately is repeated for the lifetime of many practices. I'll not fail to mention how expensive constant staff turnover becomes. Staff training and development of exceptional attitudes and skills are paramount to a healthy and happy dental practice, which, by the way, is your best marketing tool.

In my interviews with thousands of dental employees, I have found that they have certain expectations of their employers:

1. They want to know what's expected of them and how to do their job well (they want training and CE).
2. They want to be part of the decisions that directly and indirectly affect them.
3. They want a boss who is fair, strong, appreciative and effective.
4. They want supportive and team-spirited co-workers who do not gossip and whine.
5. They want equality, not favoritism, from the employer or

upper management.

6. They want a professional environment where smiles and laughter are welcomed.
7. They want compliant, appreciative patients who understand that the practice, and those in it, want the best for them.
8. They want incentives and celebrations for reaching goals and new levels of excellence.
9. They want competitive pay and benefits that increase with the success of the practice.
10. They want an employer that has a passion for the work he/she does and is generally in a happy mood.

Practice Outcomes

Satisfied employees are contingent on practice success! In our practice consultations we are hired to address and correct "practice problems" (systems), such as decreasing the failed appointments, re-engineering the schedule, decreasing accounts receivables, improving hygiene department efficiency, overhead reduction, fee evaluations, and communication skills. However, until the people problems are addressed and rectified, there's little chance that the systems improvements will last or continue to improve or stay that way.

Low office morale wreaks havoc on personal and practice success. Conversely, it's such a pleasure working with a practice that consists of mature, professional employees who respect their patients, employer(s) and co-workers and who are accountable, industrious people. When we find this environment, we congratulate them because good people find good people. Their fortunate employers have strong leadership skills. They always consider suggestions, outline their expectations, provide training, and encourage feedback. We affirm how lucky they are to have found each other and to have created the efficiency that their practice enjoys. Imagine your practice as a well-oiled machine made of three equal parts: The hygiene department, the clinical assisting department, and the administrative department. When all three parts are in sync, and all department teams are well trained and highly appreciated, the machine will run smoothly. If just one part of this machine is weak, the practice can't possibly reach its full potential in productivity. I assure you that I have seen practice productivity double in 12 to 24 months when everyone realizes that the

EMPLOYEE EVALUATION RECORD

(To be used in conjunction with the employee performance record.)

NAME	POSITION	DATE OF REVIEW

EMPLOYEE'S DEPARTMENT	IMMEDIATE SUPERVISOR	STARTING DATE

BEGINNING SALARY	CURRENT SALARY	AMOUNT OF LAST INCREASE	DATE OF LAST INCREASE

PROPOSED INCREASE	EFFECTIVE DATE

PURPOSE OF THIS REVIEW

_____ COMPLETION OF PROBATIONARY EMPLOYMENT PERIOD (90 DAYS) 　　　_____ TRANSFER

_____ FIRST PERFORMANCE REVIEW OF THE YEAR 　　　_____ MARGINAL PFRMCE REVIEW

_____ SECOND PERFORMANCE REVIEW OF THE YEAR 　　　_____ DISCIPLINARY REVIEW

_____ ANNUAL SALARY REVIEW 　　　_____ TERMINATION

SINCE EMPLOYEE'S LAST REVIEW:

_____ HAS SHOWN IMPROVEMENT

_____ HAS REMAINED THE SAME

_____ REGRESSED

WHAT IS YOUR OVERALL OPINION OF THIS EMPLOYEE?

_____ OUTSTANDING 　　　_____ FAIR

_____ VERY GOOD 　　　_____ POOR

_____ GOOD 　　　_____ **UNSATISFACTORY**

HAS THIS REVIEW BEEN DISCUSSED WITH THE EMPLOYEE?
_____ YES 　　　_____ NO 　　　IF YES, ENTER DATE _____

COMMENTS _____
_____

RECOMMEND INCREASE? _____ YES 　　　_____ NO 　　_____
　　　　　　　　　　　　　　　　　　　　　　　　　　　　SUPERVISOR'S SIGNATURE　DATE

people skills are just as important, if not more so, than the clinical or business skills of the practice. Happy teams not only create productive practices but happy dentists and patients as well. In essence, happy employees make or break the practice!

EMPLOYEE PERFORMANCE RECORD

(TO BE USED IN CONJUNCTION WITH THE **EMPLOYEE EVALUATION RECORD.**) CIRCLE THE APPROPRIATE

		HIGHEST		*LOWEST*	
PROMPTNESS ARRIVES TO WORK ON TIME	5	4	3	2	1
ABILITY TO LEARN UNDERSTANDING AND RETENTION	5	4	3	2	1
POSITION KNOWLEDGE KNOWLEDGE AND SKILLS	5	4	3	2	1
INITIATIVE ORIGINALITY AND RESOURCEFULNESS	5	4	3	2	1
JUDGMENT ABILITY TO EVALUATE SITUATIONS AND MAKE DECISIONS	5	4	3	2	1
COOPERATION WITH ASSOCIATES AND SUPERVISORS	5	4	3	2	1
ATTITUDE TOWARD JOB INTEREST AND ENTHUSIASM	5	4	3	2	1
QUANTITY OF WORK AMOUNT PRODUCED CONSISTENTLY	5	4	3	2	1
QUALITY OF WORK ACCURACY AND NEATNESS	5	4	3	2	1
WORK SPEED EMPLOYEE WORK RATE	5	4	3	2	1

MAJOR STRENGTHS   **MAJOR WEAKNESSES**

_____   _____

_____   _____

_____   _____

_____   _____

ABOUT LINDA MILES, CSP, CMC

L inda Miles, CEO of Linda Miles and Associates, a premier speaking and consulting firm in Va. Beach, VA, has enjoyed 28 years of speaking and consulting success in 50 states and on four continents. She is known as the speaker who truly understands the business and people skills of dentistry. She has written three best-selling books and dozens of audio and video productions. In 1997, Linda founded the Speaking/Consulting Network, a conference for those wishing to enhance their own speaking, consulting, and writing business. She's a 25-year member of the National Speakers Assoc., a member of the Institute of Management Consultants, the Academy of Dental Management Consultants, and the American Academy of Dental Practice Administration. She serves on the Editorial Advisory Board of Dental Practice Report and Contemporary Dental Assistant. She serves on the ADAA's Foundation and is a featured columnist in ACCESS magazine, an ADHA publication. Linda and her consultants are advisors to dental companies and military dental clinics worldwide. In March 2005, Linda received the Distinguished Service Award at the Hinman Dental Meeting. This award has been presented only 24 times in 93 years to the legends of dentistry, L.D. Pankey, Gordon Christensen and Peter Dawson to name a few.

Contact information:
Linda Miles
Linda Miles and Associates
P.O. Box 6249
Virginia Beach, VA 23456
Phone: (800) 922-0866
Email: lindamiles@cox.net
Website: www.DentalManagementU.com

C^4 Yourself:
Key Elements For
Care-driven Leadership In Dentistry

by Rhonda Mullins

"To every person there comes in their lifetime
that special moment when they are figuratively tapped on
the shoulder and offered a chance to do a very special thing,
unique to them and fitted to their talents;
What a tragedy if that moment finds them unprepared or
unqualified for the work which would be their finest hour."

—Winston Churchill

It's not about the money; it's about the relationship. Your finest hour in dentistry will come from a person or persons in whom you made a difference. This positive impact will occur because they trusted you, you spoke to their need, and you served that need with clinical expertise and, above all, because you cared. The profitability of your dental practice is the end result of your leadership effectiveness as an entrepreneur and a clinician.

Leadership does not belong exclusively to those who are so-called natural leaders. "The best leadership is that which is acquired, not that which is sired," according to Martin Luther King, Jr. For 20 years I have provided clinical and management consulting to both young and seasoned dentists, improving both their practice productivity and profitability. I have guided them strategically through business planning, practice transition, practice growth and expansions, technology integration, down-sizing, H/R management and business development. I have discovered there are four (4) key elements that are significant in creating the foundation of a successful dental practice. When these four (4) elements are consistently applied, the dentist will profit personally, professionally, and financially.

John Maxwell, author of *The 21 Irrefutable Laws of Leadership* and *17 Indisputable Laws of Teamwork*, addresses this issue:

> *Are leaders born? Of course they are. So are non-leaders. We're all born. What they are really asking is, Are some people born with gifts of leadership? Are there just natural leaders?... There are undoubtedly people who are born with leadership gifts, but there is certainly room for improvement even in people possessing natural leadership skills. These leaders still have the potential to become 10s, and 10 is tops. But those individuals, unless they cultivate their leadership, develop their skills, and continue to train, read, learn, and discipline themselves, will never be the leaders they could potentially be. The flip side is that there is no question in my mind that you CAN learn to lead if you do NOT have those natural leadership gifts.*

Leadership is a critical factor for dentists as well as the essential component to serve others and provide care at the ultimate level of need.

Effective Leadership is
- Relational *not* positional
- A Choice *not* a command
- Influence *not* title
- Discipline *not* persuasion
- Transparency *not* ambiguity
- Consistency *not* inconsistency

Only those who are completely dedicated to self-improvement in all aspects will achieve their leadership potential. Cultivating excellence in leadership allows others that are influenced by you to have greater opportunities and creates a greater capacity for change without limitations.

To succeed in dentistry today you must focus on objectives, not on obstacles, in order to thrive, excel, and acquire the capacity to lead as a clinician and entrepreneur. Remember, dentistry is what you do, leadership is who you are. It is my hope that this chapter will affect your thinking, influence your choices, and enhance your focus as a care-driven leader in your dental community.

So often in dentistry, limitations in business and patient care are a reflection of the limitations in leadership. Leadership is relational; the money is the end result, but the true measure of your effectiveness is with your employees and your patients. It's never too late to begin to create the environment that complements the vision that you have for yourself and your practice.

Evaluate where you are now, and ask yourself, "How is this working for me?" Use the chart below to pinpoint where you're starting and where you aspire to be. Effective leaders lead from the bottom, empowering others to rise up and demonstrate solid leadership and effectiveness. What I have seen over the years are three typical leadership/management styles.

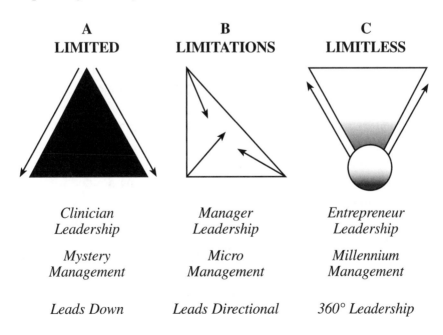

A	B	C
LIMITED	**LIMITATIONS**	**LIMITLESS**
Clinician Leadership	*Manager Leadership*	*Entrepreneur Leadership*
Mystery Management	*Micro Management*	*Millennium Management*
Leads Down	*Leads Directional*	*360° Leadership*

Clarification of styles A, B, and C

Style A Doctors—have a limit on themselves and their practice. They have placed a ceiling on how far they can grow it, the number of patients they can serve, and the retention of staff who possess leadership qualities. These doctors like to control all aspects of the practice and, they may find it hard to delegate. They may be so busy doing other personnel jobs that they are unable to produce dentistry profitably. They lead from the top down. They typically do not share any of the business functions or information with the staff and may have a hard time valuing or retaining qualified staff personnel. If you were to ask the staff about this doctor's vision, goals, or objectives, they would be a mystery to them.

Style B Doctors—there are also limitations with this style of leadership; however, not to the degree of A Doctors. Doctors in this group have a couple of key personnel to whom they can delegate responsibilities and whom they can count on, but they are still calling the shots about everything in the practice from patient care to business functions and operations. They have given some indication of their vision and dream to some of the staff, but not all. Their follow-through is not there; in other words, they have great ideas, but take no action. This doctor has a tendency to give leadership away and then take it back as soon as possible. B Doctors will lead, but inconsistently, and from many directions, trying to cover all the bases with little or no help, not because the support staff is unqualified, but because they don't know how to communicate for consistent follow-through. They make the mistake of assumption: It was done, it was handled, and it will be OK. Sometimes responsibilities will be delegated to one or two people the doctor feels are trustworthy. The doctor is challenged with having no idea what the staff is communicating to the patients, and if what the staff is communicating is a true reflection of the doctor's standard of care. This style is micro management.

Style C Doctors—there is nothing but open sky here. Members of this group have discovered how to lead. They have discovered how to accomplish this effective style by utilizing 360-degree leadership.

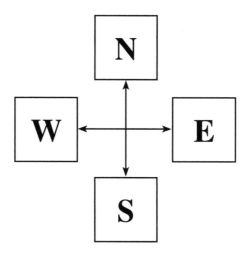

This leadership style operates like a compass. Many leaders think that leadership is leading from the top. But leadership involves *leading in all directions*. Self-leadership is about establishing the discipline first and modeling that for others. You cannot give away what you do not possess yourself, and you cannot expect from others what you yourself are not willing to be. You must be willing to acquire the discipline of self-leadership to lead in all directions. What leadership style do you model in your practice? What leadership style have you given your staff permission to demonstrate?

Now that we have evaluated your leadership style let's take the The C^4 Principal® and establish a four-step action plan to stay focused through a change process. Practicing The C^4 Principal® will facilitate staying on purpose daily with regard to delegation, decisions, and direction. Keeping it simple is key.

The C^4 Principal® will allow you to do just that. Keep it simple and stay focused! Benefit your patients, your people, and yourself!

C^1: CREDIBILITY

As a credible president and CEO of your enterprise, your management style has to be balanced between being a responsible leader and dentist.

Your trustworthiness, which is the sum of your integrity and sincerity, generates the transparency and credibility which, in turn, attract loyalty and respect from your patients and employees.

Integrity and sincerity are demonstrated through honesty, self-control, fairness, concern for others, and a commitment to keeping promises. Others around you will either embrace your new standard of leadership or they will remove themselves from the environment.

C^2: COMMUNICATION

Communication is the most important and essential leadership skill one has to master. Why not communications first and credibility second? I have discovered that the character of people and their credibility stems from a standard of core values. These standards and value systems are something that was instilled long before one becomes a dentist. So foundationally, credibility must be in place first.

I was very privileged to have a person pour invaluable information into me and coach me on communicating. She told me, *"Effective communication is the willingness to be uncomfortable enough to produce the results."* People usually will tell everyone else what they want or think, without telling the one person who could do something about the issue. There is a tendency in leadership sometimes to circumvent. Therefore, as you evaluate this area of your leadership, be intrusive with yourself. If you're not sure of your truth and openness in communicating, ask your wife or husband, your partner, or your staff. Remember the scene in the movie, *A Few Good Men* when Jack Nicholson's character was on the stand, and, when asked by Tom Cruise's character to tell the truth, his infamous response was, *"You can't handle the truth!"* Yet he spilled the beans, with the attitude that he was above reproach. Well, you know the rest of the story. Be humble and willing to hear the truth for your benefit, the benefit of those that support you, and the benefit of those you serve.

To lead effectively you must communicate effectively. Here are four steps to achieve your goal of improving this area:

1. *Cultivate a clear style: Learning*

   a. Words

   b. Tone

   c. Body Language

   d. Direct Purposeful Experience

Staff and employees in your dental practice will learn and retain 7 percent by reading, 38 percent by listening, 55 percent by watching, and 80 percent by participating.

   2. Cultivate a cogent style

   a. Communicate to drive convincingly to the point.

   b. Communicate to bring your staff together; they need to hear the same thing, at the same time.

   3. Cultivate naturalness

   a. Find your comfort zone. They way I communicate may not be natural to you, but if the results are just as effective, that's all that matters. Everyone's natural, comfortable way of communicating will differ.

   b. Find the right words. Keep it simple. Big words or a huge vocabulary are not necessary for effective communications.

   c. Find the right time and environment. Timing is everything when making sure someone is listening. Also, this key point tells others the best time for them to approach you to communicate, when you will be available both physically and emotionally.

   4. Cultivate persuasiveness

   a. Focus on Benefits. Ask more than tell, when communicating to get others to embrace your recommendation or treatment.

When my husband was the technical director for Johnson and Johnson's, Ceramco Division, the marketing and technical divisions collaborated on launching a new product. They believed that, if the marketing theme communicated the superiority of this new product and its value and benefits to the industry, the sales force would also be convinced and then the customers. Therefore, as my husband and his colleagues entered their office each day, they saw a huge banner that read "Benefit the Customer." That banner served as a constant reminder of the importance of making sure that this policy was always at the forefront as they began this campaign. Today, that product has changed the industry.

This step makes or breaks your case acceptance ratio. When presenting or recommending restorative dentistry, many dentists feel the need to justify their treatment or recommendation versus focusing on the benefits of the treatment to the patient. Don't be one of them.

Enrollment steps for recommending treatment.
1. Relationship—Eye contact (3 seconds to 3 minutes to form an impression)
   a. Touch an arm or shoulder to convey trust
2. Need/Value—Speaking with a sense of urgency
   a. Ask open-ended questions
   b. Find out what is important to your patients. (Create value)
3. Choice—Create an opportunity for your patients to decide
   a. Speak to the obvious—The other person's response will tell you what his or her concerns are. If financial, offer a solution (example: third party financing options)
4. Acceptance—When establishing effective communications it takes two.
   a. When making others accountable to come into agreement with you for change, there are three options:
      i. Accept—Surrender what has kept you from moving ahead
      ii. Deny—Hold firm for new standard
      iii. Negotiate—Find a common ground to make it work. What's the preferred end result? Benefit the patients. Benefit the practice.

How can you tell if you're improving communication? Examine this flow pattern and see how your communication effectiveness influences others on a day-to-day basis and how this component is vital to transforming every aspect of your business. (Indicate the boxes where improvement is needed.)

Internal Communications:
1. Leadership delegation
2. Practice representation

3. Employee job description
4. Patient perception

This illustration shows how communicating goes beyond a face-to-face conversation and the long-term benefits to practice growth, business development, and leadership. Here we can see the routing of a conversation from the first contact of a phone call to a patient referring a patient and then a doctor referring a doctor.

❏ PS	❏ SS	❏ SD
Patient to Staff	*Staff to Staff*	*Staff to Doctor*
❏ PP	❏ DD	❏ DS
Patient to Patient	*Doctor to Doctor*	*Doctor to Staff*
❏ SP	❏ PD	❏ DP
Staff to Patient	*Patient to Doctor*	*Doctor to Patient*

Ask your accountability coach to listen to you in these areas, in actual circumstances. Immediately apply the coaching changes to the next opportunity in both areas. Then remember: the three "R's:

Recount—The experience
Repeat—Go for repetition
Role—You're the lead

After daily accountability and feedback from those involved in those areas of your practice, you should begin to make adjustments in your behavior so that others will interact with you, not react to you. Once you go forward, you won't go back.

5. Acknowledge—Show & tell, not sell! This distinction will set you apart from the pack.
    a. Acknowledge others
    b. Create new relationship standard
    c. Ask for consistent feedback

C^3: COMPETENCE

"Your premium brand had better be delivering something special or it's not going to get the business."

—Warren Buffet

Last year when an acquaintance had gotten sick and could not fulfill an obligation to speak for a group of Atlanta businesswomen, I had the privilege to stand in and was allowed a view from the top. This is a woman who has accomplished a great deal, overcome a great deal, and she is recognized as one of the first in her field to rise to the top without compromising her standard of leadership or core values. She and her leadership style adhere to those core values each day. After having had the vision and making the investment for years, she delivered something so special that Warren Buffet bought her company. When you catch someone like Warren Buffet's eye for business, respect and value are immediate. Other people want what you have to offer. Are you delivering something special to your business?

The areas of your competence are vital to you and to everyone around you. Stay current in your ability to provide cutting-edge dentistry. Invest in an upper level training program, research new products, and learn new things that will add value to yourself and to what you do for your patients. You can't give what you don't have. Self-leadership is the ability to make more of you available to others.

1. Demonstrate Excellence in Clinical Expertise
    a. Serve patients exceptionally
    b. Stay focused

    c. Stay challenged

    d. Set yourself apart

2. Demonstrate sound decision making

    a. Delegate with accountability

    b. Deal with difficulties with diplomacy

    c. Diminish the drama in the office

    d. Distinguish leadership by directness

3. Demonstrate entrepreneurism

    a. Clarity of business

        i. Know your leadership style

        ii. Know your numbers

        iii. Get outside objectivity to make changes

        iv. Create a vision, goals, and objectives

    b. Cut Overhead –Two Options

        i. Downsize

        ii. Focus on the benefits and schedule the treatment

    c. Construct H/R structure (policy manual)

        i. Trust in you will result in loyalty and longevity

C^3 Competence will take time and organization to develop a strategic plan. Do not be defeated or discouraged, and stay focused on the benefits to your practice.

C^4: CARE

It's all about the relationship when it comes to the driving force of why you do what you do. This element should be a reflection of who you are. This four-letter word speaks loudly when referencing a style of leadership.

"The huge turnout for Live 8 here and around the world proves that, thanks to the leadership from people like Tony Blair and Gordon Brown, the world is beginning to demand more action on global health."

—Bill Gates

All the money in the world and Bill Gates brings it home in this quote: people caring, taking action for health, and providing care to others. This whole effort was and is about being care-driven.

1. What are you passionate about?

2. What is your driving force?
3. Would others say you are care-driven?
4. Do you love doing dentistry because it provides significance to others, or do you love doing dentistry because it provides success to you?

The Thesaurus gives the words *attention* and *treatment* as alternate words to describe care. The dictionary definitions of care include close attention, to heed, a liking or regard, a responsibility. Care is responsibility.

What people say about you when you are not around is more significant than what they say when you are. How you act when no one is looking is more significant than when someone is watching. Being a care-driven leader today may not be able to be measured in benefits today, tomorrow, or the next day, or next month, or even next year. When you make the investment of a care-driven mindset, the benefits will be measured by dollars because a business is attached to the care. The core need of others is to know they are valued!

C^4CARE allows others to feel valued. It's simple. Keep that in the forefront of your leadership and you will thrive, professionally and financially.

Begin to ask the questions that will change others' perception of you as a dentist, employer, business person. Care is an action word. It requires demonstration for others to feel it. As Emeril would say "Do you feel the love?" So many times when I walk into an office to begin an assessment, I say to myself, "there's no love happening here!"

Usually, you as the owner of your practice can see what needs to happen, but you're unable to mobilize everyone to create the movement that unifies and synchronizes everyone and everything to hit the mark, reach the goals, and meet the objectives.

Exceptional leaders discover where they are at (point "A") before they present an action plan to get to where they need to be (point "B").

Acquire the information. Ask your staff, ask your patients, use open-ended questions, and use a third party if you have to. Surveys have indicated that most people leave practices because of issues with the staff, not the doctor. It is very important as a doctor that you know what is being done and said to your patients. If you are care-driven, and others around you are not, "Houston, we have a problem."

Don't be fearful of what response you may get. In fact, seek it out. Although confronting the truth can be difficult and painful, you can make the adjustments needed in your standard of service and care, which is an extension of you and your leadership. Take it to the next level. Let your people and your patients experience C^4CARE in your office starting today. C^4 yourself!

ABOUT RHONDA MULLINS

*R*honda is CEO of VistaPro Consulting, Inc. a healthcare consulting firm in Atlanta, Georgia that helps dentists change lives through care-driven leadership and care-driven focused environments. Rhonda brings 29 years of expertise and the endorsement of satisfied clients as a coach and consultant. Her transparency as a leader in dental knowledge, communications, and enrollment skills benefits her clients beyond their expectations. Her coaching and consulting have yielded abundant profits from the investment doctors make in themselves and their practices. Her objective: Turning your success into significance in dentistry, coaching practices and people to hit the mark in leadership, clinical aesthetic dentistry growth and development with a care-driven approach, and strategic enterprise development—long term. Experience in dental technology, contextual leadership training, practice development, management and transition strategies, sets her apart from the ordinary. A national speaker and communication specialist, Rhonda has been featured in Contemporary Esthetics and Restorative Practice magazine and has been the keynote speaker at national dental conventions over the last seven years. She is a member and/or affiliate of the Academy of Dental Management Consultants, National Businesswomen's Association, and the American Society for Training & Development.

Contact Information:
Rhonda G. Mullins
VistaPro Consulting
400 East Point Drive
Canton, GA 30115
Phone: (770) 720-1766
Email: rho2ceo@adelphia.net
Website: www.rhondamullins.com

THE REALMS OF POSSIBILITY
FOR LEADERSHIP

by Lisa Philp, RDH, CMC

Have you ever wondered what it takes to make it to the top in dentistry? To be one of those dentists who has it all—strong leadership presence, a high-performing team, financial freedom, solid patient relationships, an exciting career, boundless enthusiasm and energy? Our experience of coaching dental teams and their leaders has shown distinct characteristics that are directly related to achieving such success. Different people have differing ideas about success. Some think in terms of money, others in terms of accomplishments, while others in terms of love and happiness. One definition of success is an ongoing process of setting goals and achieving them. Success is a continuous experience and not some remote destination to be reached someday. It does not matter what our goals are (money, love, power, fame), when we achieve our goals we experience success.

"Leadership is an invisible strand as mysterious as it is powerful. No combination of talents can guarantee it. The qualities are found in the poor and the rich, the humble and the proud, the common man and the brilliant thinker. Leadership's imperative is knowing when to advance and when to pause, when to criticize and when to praise, how to encourage others to excel."

—Marie Marquies du Deffond

The common characteristics, traits, and skills that successful leaders possess lie within the following realms. The first realm begins with personal development and self-awareness. The second realm is the ability to build a high-performing team in combination with the third realm of understanding leadership styles and their impact on results. The fourth and fifth realms of listening skills and organizational systems make for a well-rounded, solid leader.

The five realms are based on some fundamental beliefs.

It All Starts at the Top

"It all starts at the top" is not just a cliché. The top is where the direction and support come from by combining the right moves, training, timing, and, most important, the right attitude.

Progress Involves Risk

Progress involves risk; many dental practices get stuck doing things the old way, because it is comfortable, and limit their impact on progress. Change is a fact of life. We can't steal second base with our foot still on first!

Put People First and the Money Will Come to Buy the Things

When we put people first by establishing rapport, building relationships, and showing sincere interest in understanding their needs before our own, we create more revenue and profit than from any other action. One of the most profound statements ever spoken about healthcare philosophy was by Patch Adams of the Gesundheit Institute who said, *"You treat a disease, you win or lose. You treat a person, you win every time, no matter what the outcome."*

The Possibilities Are Endless with a Strong Group of Leaders

The challenge for dentists lies in juggling roles because of the many hats they must wear to survive as a leader—the owner, the financial manager, the human resource expert, and the main revenue generator that needs to be busy working on patients, just to mention a few. They set the course for the health of the business, the health of the patients, and the health of the team. Leadership starts at the top but can't end at the top. No dentist can be successful without a team. He must be able to duplicate his vision and build a strong team of leaders, in order to access all possibility.

In 1995 the appearance of Daniel Goleman's work with Emotional

Intelligence Interpersonal Skills, and the fact that research could quantify, with evidence, the direct correlation between the impact of personality, behaviors and fulfillment in the workplace, were huge revelations. He showed that good relationships and coping strategies are the key to our success in every area of human activity from childhood, to being a good employee, to a leader who can bring out the best in their employee's.

"Social science" has finally caught up to scientific data and rationality. Mainstream educators, business people, and the media have shown that emotional intelligence is not a fad or a trend in modern day leadership; it is fundamental to success.

The First Realm—Personal Development

Personal development involves our openness to looking within at our own people skills and emotional intelligence in interacting with others. Using self-awareness and self-management involves the willingness to read our emotions and why we are feeling the way we are, as well as the impact of our behaviors on others. We must be willing to look at our real abilities rather than fixate on just one or two aspects of who we think we are. Our positive self-worth creates our ability to appreciate the diversity within ourselves. The ability to trust and take responsibility for our actions, as well as strive to overcome the obstacles, drives us to reach excellence. An interesting aspect of trust is that people who have the highest self-esteem find it easier to trust others. When we are confident in our own abilities, the fear of trusting others is diminished. When we have a high level of self-esteem, we are more likely to share problems or feelings with a friend or companion. On the other hand, if our self-esteem is fragile, we will worry about what others think of us and we will keep problems and feelings to ourselves. The self-empowered person finds it easier to trust because his/her self-esteem and confidence does not depend upon the approval of others.

A leader must also understand and be aware of the causes and effects of actions taken or not taken. This capacity of attention is called responsibility or the ability to respond. The Chinese Book of Changes, the I Ching, tells us that *"It is not the event that is important; it is the response to the event that is everything."* This is also referred to by Stephen Covey as Pro-activity: Choosing our actions, rather than controlling or being controlled by them. Responsible people take responsibility for shaping their future and for initiating behavior that will create the situations they want. Responsible people do not wait to see what will happen; they see that they are a causative influence on their environment rather than a victim. Our ability to respond impeccably and with integrity to the events we create brings out the leader within.

The power to overcome all obstacles is a human resource that is often equated with the use of energy or the empowerment of self and others. When we demonstrate our power, no one can tell us what can't be done. We are freed from patterns of self-diminishment and are less likely to accept other people's perceptions of what we can and cannot do. We all possess our own personal power, duplicated nowhere else on the planet. No two individuals carry the same combination of talents or challenges; therefore, when we compare ourselves to others, this is a sign that we do not believe we can achieve our goals. This attitude affects not only ourselves, but extends to everyone we come into contact with.

"When a team becomes more aligned, a commonality of direction emerges, and individuals emerge harmonized. There is less wasted energy. In fact, a resonance or synergy develops, like the coherent light of a laser rather than the incoherent and scattered light of a light bulb."

—Peter Senge, *The Fifth Discipline*

The Second Realm—Developing a High-Performing Team

This is the ability to develop a high-performing team with the capabilities of empathy and empowerment by ensuring that we have the right people on the bus. All teams are a two-way mirror reflection of their leaders. Quite often, the issues that a leader has with a dysfunctional or under-performing team, are the very same traits, behaviors and characteristics that the team complains about in the leader. The dentist leader has many demands and must wear many different hats: the owner, the team leader, operational director, technical service provider, and the main revenue generator. Assessing leadership style and how it sets the stage for the culture and climate gives the freedom from having to do it all. Creating and building a cohesive team with a common set of values, purpose, and vision is significantly and directly related to the overall health of the practice.

Empathy is understanding what others might be feeling or thinking so that we can see their perspective. Seeing the world through their eyes allows us to see the diversity and relate to them in an enhanced way. The coach of a championship team, for example, gets the best from players by placing them at different positions to assess their potential rather than insisting they always play the position for which they were hired. When we are willing to look again at someone else's world, we stay open and flexible toward others and ourselves.

To empower people, we must give them the authority to make decisions and to act without having to get approval every time. It means allowing people to use their own intelligence, experience, intuition, and creativity to help the business improve and succeed. Empowerment means keeping people informed and involved in the operations of the organization. It means listening to people and using their ideas.

The right person has more to do with character traits and innate capabilities than with specific knowledge, background, or skills. We need to take the time to define the characteristics of what constitutes the right person, for our environment and team.

Jim Collins, author of *Good To Great*, tells us that in order to survive in today's business we must get the wrong people off the bus and the right people on the bus in the right seats. When looking for the right person, it will help to look at three key areas of characteristics. They include role-specific duties, relationship and communication skills, and attitude.

Role-specific duties relate to what seat on the bus needs to be filled. Can the team members follow protocols and are they trainable? Are they comfortable with accountability and able to ask for help as needed? Do they take pride in accuracy and quality?

Their relationship and communication skills are especially important as they are in a healthcare field serving patients. Some assessment questions may include:

- Are they people focused with a genuine interest in building relationships to gain trust?
- Can they express themselves clearly and defend a position they believe in?
- Are they good listeners or do they interrupt?

The most important characteristic is their attitude. It is the quality most challenging to change or modify. Peoples' attitudes and behaviors are driven by their self-image and self-worth. How they feel about success, about money, about achievement, right and wrong. These are more important than educational status, money, mistakes, success, appearance, and skill. Questions to ask are:

- Do they focus on others or are they self-absorbed?
- Are they willing to go the extra mile to meet the team objective?
- Are they self-starters with a positive outlook on life?
- Are they always looking to learn and improve, viewing their role as a career, not just a job?
- Are they comfortable with change?

The right people, who answer the above questions in ways that match a team culture, will succeed with the leader's support in creating a compelling vision. An environment that encourages regular feedback as well as listening, provides them with an understanding of how their roles fit into the bigger picture. They also need the freedom to think, express and act, to question policies and procedures that interfere with quality or service, and to experiment and innovate.

Truly excellent businesses accomplish success through the efforts of the people who make up the team. The solid team will consistently achieve its goals, provide excellent care and service, keep up with or stay ahead of the market changes, and satisfy patients' needs and expectations.

The Third Realm—Understanding Leadership Styles

The consulting firm of Hay/McBer in conjunction with Dr. Daniel Golemen performed one of the first quantitative studies in which they drew a random sample of 3,871 executives from a database of 20,000 members. They found that there are six different leadership styles that directly impact team behaviors and the culture of a work environment. They also discovered that leaders with the most success were the ones who didn't depend on just one style, but were able to adjust their style based on each individual business situation.

The Coercive Style

A dental practice was a sole practitioner environment with eight team members in total. The team generally was a cohesive group and all personal friends. The practice was financially healthy for a number of years. The practice was extremely busy with three full-time hygienists and 3,500 active patients. The team felt that they had enough patients, and, because of their volume, they didn't see the need to market and grow the practice with new patients or devote any energy to existing patients because they would always be loyal and stay at the practice.

Then one day a new dentist moved into town and quickly became a major competitor. Their patients began requesting their records to be transferred to the new dentist at an alarming rate, and they lost 1,000 patients in the first year. The practice was in crisis mode. The new dentist's facility was modern, state-of-the-art, and could accommodate appointments within two weeks as opposed to two months. Production began falling and the schedule had hours of voids each week. The practice value was diminishing although the team felt they were doing their best to stop the bleeding.

The dentist/leader became desperate and was determined to turn things around and deal with the erosion. He called an emergency meeting and told the team that they needed to change, what to do to change, and told them if things didn't get better they would be out of a job. If they didn't adhere to his orders they would be reprimanded and/or written up. The dentist in this case used a coercive style of *"do what I tell you,"* because of the crisis. He created a reign of terror, demeaning his staff, and passing on his anxiety when the day didn't run smoothly.

Although this tactic did cause a turn around short-term—production began stabilizing and the team worked to fill the voids in the schedule—morale was at an all-time low, and two key team members defected to the competition down the street. The team members didn't want to share any ideas, lost all sense of responsibility, and actually became sabotagers, saying *"I am not doing anything more to help him."* There was no commitment and team members were alienated from each other. Their roles became "just a job" in a high-stress environment.

Given the example above, we can see the impact of this style of leading by fear and threats. We would think it should never be used. However, there is a small place for it, but it should be used only with extreme caution in a few situations. It will work only when there are problem employees from the beginning and when desperate change is needed, when all else fails. Once the emergency has passed, it is time to use another style to suit the environment.

The Authoritative Style

A dental practice was a new dental practice start-up. It was opened from scratch and had twelve patient charts on the first day. Everyone on the team was aware that there would be a lot of growth and building to do. Six months after opening, the team evaluated their goals and realized that they had built the patient base to only 200 patients. They became concerned and wondered what could be done to expedite the growth. The dentist became worried as his loan payments were due and he was in a financial crunch. The leader recognized that the team needed a new course. The leader facilitated meetings once a week for several hours with the intent of mobilizing the team toward a common vision. They spent time developing a mission statement, taking into account all team members' values. They spent time writing goals for each week and defining each person's description of the role each would play in the practice growth. Once this plan was in place, the dentist managed to get the team members focusing on the future, not on the past six months of what they thought was failure. The team developed a marketing plan that was driven by "what does the patient want?" They analyzed the current patients' expectations and identified the wants of the consumer as the primary goal of daily operations, instead of focusing on what the practice needed.

Their focus and plan caused changes to come quickly, and within months the practice was building, with 75 new patients a month. The team felt respected and took ownership for their role in the success of meeting the patients' needs, and the dentist acknowledged their contribution with a team event. The authoritative style used here by the leader had a positive impact on a work environment and drove up morale by focusing on a vision, the future, and not making the team feel as if they were to blame for the past. The authoritative leader is a visionary; he/she motivates people by making it clear how they fit into the larger vision. The team understands that what they do matters, and why.

The Affiliative Style

The affiliative style has a primary focus of trust and inspiration. This style can be demonstrated in a situation with a large group practice with three partners and 21 team members. The practice had just terminated a long-term office manager, who took credit for the employees' work and pitted one team member against another. The team was run down, suspicious, and wary about the future. They wondered who was going to replace the previous manager and how they wouldn't like whoever it may be. The dentists were not communicating what was going to happen, which caused more stress, and the daily operations were in chaos due to lack of direction and communication.

Eventually, they hired a new office manager who had a challenge to win over the team and get them over the past experience with the previous manager. The new manager was determined to use an affiliative style and a "people come first" approach. She spent her first three months interviewing team members, listening to their past experiences and ideas of how they could be more effective in their role.

She organized the departments into regular meetings and taught them how to create productive agendas, and she worked to earn their trust. She managed to adjust the rules to match the individual team members and built strong emotional bonds. They shared ideas and were creative with solutions to inspire innovation. She gave them the freedom to do their jobs in the way they thought was most effective with regular, positive feedback.

Coercive	**Authoritative**	**Affiliative**
Demands immediate compliance	Mobilizes people toward a vision	Creates harmony and builds emotional bonds
The style in a phrase:		
"Do what I tell you."	"Come with me."	"People come first."
Underlying emotional intelligence competencies:		
Drive to achieve, initiative, self-control	Self-confidence, empathy, change catalyst	Empathy, building relationships, communication
When the style works best:		
In a crisis, to kick start a turnaround, or with problem employees	When changes require a new vision, or when a clear direction is needed	To heal rifts in a team or to motivate people during stressful circumstances
Overall impact on climate:		
Negative	Most strongly positive	Positive

Reprinted by permission of *Harvard Business Review* (excerpt)
From Leadership That Gets Results – by Daniel Goleman
March-April 2000 R00204

The Democratic Style

An example of a democratic leadership style is demonstrated in the example of a dental practice we worked with in the southern United States. The practice was owned by a husband and wife team in a small town of 500 people. They had an extremely loyal team and a large patient base. The practice was functioning well and the leaders involved the team in all decisions. At first the democratic style was working well and the team enjoyed being asked for their opinions. Then two members relocated out of the area and the team couldn't find replacements. They were all chipping in to pick up the slack, and, after four months, they became exhausted with the long hours and got behind in their duties.

The dentists continued to use a democratic style and ask their team's opinions on what should be done. It became evident that the team disliked being asked what to do by the leader when they didn't know. Morale began to drop, and the team judged the leader negatively for not having the answers. They felt it was time for the leader to give direction and stop depending on them for every decision. They began to ask for raises, demand performance reviews, and refused to participate in the team meetings.

The overly democratic leaders couldn't understand why the team felt this way and why they all of a sudden needed feedback and direction. The doctor and his wife felt that the team should know how they were doing without having to be told after every decision. These leaders did not see that, even though the team was involved in the direction of the practice, they still experienced situations when they needed to look to a leader for guidance and direction. Often business owners have to make decisions before asking the team's opinion. The democratic approach is detrimental when the team does not have the tools needed to guide decisions being made.

This style's impact on the work environment can be effective when the members know what to do to solve a problem. It is not as popular as some of the other styles because of the exasperating consequences of endless meetings where ideas are mulled over, consensus remains elusive, and the only visible result is scheduling more meetings. Some democratic leaders use this style to put off making crucial decisions, hoping that thrashing things out will eventually yield a blinding insight. In reality, their people end up feeling confused and leaderless. Such an approach can even escalate conflicts.

The Pacesetting Style

Take the case of a Karen, a new associate who joined a dental practice. She immediately set extremely high standards and demonstrated the standards daily. She had superb technical ability, built loyal patients, and was the person everyone turned to for help. She developed numerous programs, including a periodontal program for hygiene and a treatment planning program for large cases. She communicated these programs daily and was continually looking for ways to perform better and faster. She asked the same of everyone around her, but was quick to pinpoint her co-worker's mistakes. When team members made mistakes, she jumped in and took over because she could do it better. She was destroying the morale without knowing it. The team felt that she expected them to know what to do without direction and found themselves second-guessing what she wanted. They were burned out and didn't feel like they were trusted to make decisions for themselves.

This leadership style works well when everyone on the team needs little direction and is a self-motivated professional. With this type of team in place, leaders with a pacesetting style are able to get projects done on time and ahead of schedule.

The Coaching Style

Of the six styles, the coaching style is used the least, but it could prove to be the most effective towards developing a positive environment and getting results. Let's look at a dental practice that had a high-performing team, was coasting along doing what they had done for years, and got stuck on a financial plateau for two years. The leader decided that they needed an outside coach. The coach came into the practice and worked with the team to identify their unique strengths and weaknesses and how these related to their personal and career aspirations. She taught them long-term development goals and helped them conceptualize a plan for attaining them. They made agreements with each other on each person's role and responsibilities in enacting the plan. The coach gave ample instructions and feedback. She also delegated challenging assignments, even if that meant the tasks wouldn't be accomplished quickly. She was willing to put up with short-term failure for the sake of long-term learning.

When employees know that a coach will observe them, and they care, they feel free to show initiative. The implicit message is, "I believe in you, I'm investing in you, and I expect your best efforts." Employees very often rise to the challenge with their heart, mind, and soul.

Democratic	Pacesetting	Coaching
The leader's modus operandi:		
Forges consensus through compliance	Sets high standards for performance	Develops people for the future
The style in a phrase:		
"What do you think?"	"Do as I do, now."	"Try this."
Underlying emotional intelligence competencies:		
Collaboration, team leadership, communication	Conscientiousness, drive to achieve, initiative	Developing others, empathy, self-awareness
When the style works best:		
To build buy-ins or consensus, or to get input from valuable employees	To get quick results from a highly motivated and competent team	To help an employee improve performance or develop long-term strengths
Overall impact on climate:		
Positive	Negative	Positive

Reprinted by permission of *Harvard Business Review* (excerpt)
From Leadership That Gets Results – by Daniel Goleman
March-April 2000 R00204

The most positive style as far as impact on the success of a business is the authoritative style. The other positive styles depending on the situation are affiliative, democratic and coaching. The key to effective leadership is to understand your dominant style and how it serves your purpose and then look at which other styles would be worth learning, based on your individual situation.

The Fourth Realm—Listening Skills

Communication is comprised of 10 percent words, 30 percent tone of voice, and 60 percent non-verbal behavior. Listening is defined as the accurate perception of what is being communicated to you. It is a two-way exchange in which both parties involved must always be receptive to the thoughts, ideas and emotions of the other. Listening does not come naturally to everyone and is not just two people taking turns talking.

There are many barriers that get in the way of effective listening in the dental office. Some of these barriers include a hectic schedule with last minute emergencies, difficult patients, the pressure of running on time, and the inability to relax and cope with stress. If we are rigid in thought processes and mind-set and not open to hearing another person's point of view, or we talk too much and dominate the conversation, we put up barriers that prevent effective listening.

Some strategies to overcome these barriers include setting uninterrupted time to communicate with others and making sure we are present (attentive) when in a communication cycle with the other person. Tune out the world and tune in the person who is speaking. It is important to listen to emotions as well as words. We need to give feedback on what we hear, to make sure that we understand the other person's perspective. The ability to read people is an art that can be taught and learned, considering 60 percent of a message is in body language.

There are two types of listening—passive and active. Passive listening consists of acknowledgements, door openers, and silence.

Acknowledgments are a type of receptive listening that tells the sender that we are receiving the message without judgment and interruption. It shows that we are attentive and interested in what they have to say, not what we want to say. Some examples of acknowledgments are *"Really," "Wow," "Uh huh," "Hmmm," "I see,"* and *"I agree."*

Door openers are tools that encourage a person to continue speaking or telling you about themselves. If you allow a person to finish a message without interrupting and encourage the sender to go on and get it all out, he or she will be much more attentive when it is your turn to send a message. Some examples of door openers include: *"Go on," "Please continue,"* and *"Tell me more,"* and *"Then what?"*

Silence is a very powerful communication skill in relating to others. Careful pauses in the conversation give people time to organize their thoughts, to gain the confidence to go on and to express their deeper feelings. Silence is a potent tool for getting people to talk about what's bothering them, and talking to someone who is willing to listen may be just the encouragement a person needs. The most challenging part of silence is asking a question and then waiting for the person to respond, without speaking first. When you ask a question, be quiet. Wait for an answer, even if a few moments of silence occur.

Active listening is the single most effective listening skill you can use to calm an irate person, to defuse anger, to handle a difficult person, or, on the other hand, to enhance a good relationship. This kind of listening requires effort and discipline. Active listening is the act of giving feedback on what we think we have heard the other person saying, to make sure that we have heard correctly. A simple repetition or paraphrasing is not sufficient. The listener should demonstrate, in his/her own words, an adequate understanding of the content, intent, and emotion of the speaker's remarks.

The key reason for learning listening skills is to help keep misunderstandings to a minimum and to ensure that we listen with sincerity, understanding, acceptance, and caring. We need to listen to our teams and to our patients and be open-minded about communication.

The profession of dentistry needs people to thrive, no matter what our specific goals. We have an opportunity every day to exchange emotion—or communication—both verbal and nonverbal. We can choose to ignore the chances to enrich our relationships or solve everyday problems constructively and simply.

"Our system does not depend on the greatness of one top leader, or even on the thin crust of top leadership. It depends on a deep and broad stratum of leaders at every level and throughout every segment of the society." —John Gardener

The Fifth Realm—Organizational Systems

The operational model of a dental practice consists of five engines that house 21 key performance indicators or drivers. All drivers are affected by the health of the systems that operate every day. The systems help us operate in an orderly and efficient manner. We have systems for how we drive a car, how we elect our leaders, how we are educated, and how we run our homes. If one part or person doesn't follow the system, situations arise that cause stress. Systems help us to gain control of a situation or our environment; they give us predictability and produce optimally consistent results.

There are 44 systems that the leader needs to be in tune with for a well-functioning practice. The process of measuring how the systems are working and applying three elementary rules serve as a way to prioritize what may need to be changed or left alone.

Rule 1—If something is working, then continue and find ways to do more of it.

Rule 2—If something is not working, do something different.

Rule 3—If you don't know if it works, find out.

Remember, leadership ability resides within all of us and starts with you. With your mission in mind, the toughest opponent you'll face isn't an upset patient, difficult case, or competition. It is the voice inside your head that says, *"That's not good enough!"* As you strive to do better, you'll always be able to say that you work because you love what you do—and patients and team members will feel your enthusiasm.

"Self-esteem isn't everything; it's just that there's nothing without it."

—Gloria Steinem

ABOUT LISA PHILP, RDH, CMC

L isa Philp is the President of Transitions Group North America, the practice development division of Benco Dental. She graduated from East Tennessee State University as a Registered Dental Hygienist. As a leader and coach, she has been instrumental in the creation and development of numerous customized client programs that have been designated approved under the PACE Program by the Academy of General Dentistry and has coached hundreds of dental practices through their success transition. Lisa is a certified facilitator in Integrity Selling, a Certified Management Consultant as designated by the Academy of Dental Management Consultants, has been recognized in the National Register's Who's Who in Canadian Dentistry and is a leading speaker for major manufacturers, dental meetings, study clubs, laboratories, and professional associations. She is the Director of Team Training for Canada's Millennium Aesthetics Programs, and is a key opinion leader with Benco Dental, CareCredit, Philips Oral Health Care (Canada) Ltd., and Dentsply Canada Ltd. She currently provides training to students at the University of Toronto, Faculty of Dentistry and is a guest lecturer at the University of Western Ontario and the University of Montreal. Her articles have been published in leading publications. Lisa's mission is to make dentistry simple and fun, allowing dental professionals to achieve personal and professional fulfillment in the workplace.

Contact Information:

Lisa Philp
Transitions Group North America
3050 Harvester Road, Suite 205
Burlington, ON
L7N 3J1 Canada
Phone: (800) 345-5157
Email: lphilp@tcgdds.com

WHAT GOES AROUND COMES AROUND:
Keep practice communication on track with the Awareness Wheel

by Shari Tastad RDH, B.S.

Congratulations! You have just completed a very productive morning schedule. You're feeling great! Your career in dentistry is just what you dreamed it would be. Or is it?

You reluctantly walk into a staff meeting (not your favorite part of owning a practice) and "it" begins. You remind your hygienist to take digital photos on recare patients. In a flash, arms go up, eye contact intensifies, her face turns red, and she frantically replies, "I don't have time." Communication quickly comes to a standstill, and you decide that it just isn't worth spending more time on this issue. You retreat and decide you will do it on your own (or not at all). This recurring breakdown of communication has confirmed to you that staff meetings are a waste of time.

Communication is a tool that we take for granted and something we don't learn in dental school. It takes practice. And it's worth the work. The ability to process and facilitate "people information" (information about self, others, and your interactions) will bring you more meaningful experiences, good feelings, and better connections with others than any other skill. To build this skill requires awareness. Clear communication involves being able to verbalize what you observe, think, feel, want, and are willing to do.

Good solutions to topical, personal, and relational issues grow out of the rich soil of complete and congruent awareness of self and others. For complete and honest communication, it is important to start with five key pieces of information: what you see, think, feel, want, and are willing to do. All five are distinct yet interact with each other. By using a tool called "The Awareness Wheel," you can learn to more effectively process important information about yourself and others.

In the above staff meeting the doctor asked the hygienist to take digital photos (what the doctor wanted) and the hygienist said she had no time (what she was thinking). Many pieces of the communication are missing from this interaction that would have helped each person understand each other at a deeper level and improve communication in the office. The more you know about yourself and others at any moment, the more effective you will communicate in a wide variety of critical situations. As a leader you are the person to make the difference. By learning to bridge impasses, you will initiate change within your dental office.

Observing: What do you observe about yourself and the other person? Observations include verbal and non-verbal data taken in through the senses: sight, sound, touch, smell, and taste. Your senses are like a good journalist; they observe, report, and describe, but they do not interpret. There are three major elements in spoken communications, though they have a disproportionate impact on what is received and believed. What is actually said accounts for only a fraction of the message; we put more stock in the way something is said, its vocal and tonal message. Remember the admonishment from your mother: it's not what you say; it's how you say it. But by far the greatest influence in communication is the visual impact (what is seen). Without ever hearing a word, you make meaning from various kinds of visual data: context, time, space, texture, design, accessories, clothing, and body language, among others.

In our initial scenario of the staff meeting, the doctor might have noticed the hygienist's rate of speech, her intense eyes, her flushed skin, and the intensity in her voice. The hygienist might have noticed the dentist's posture, composure, and the tone of his voice. Look and listen for signs in yourself and the other person.

Tips to consider:
1. Notice individual patterns. Everybody has a body signature.
2. Let yourself see and hear all the data.
3. Pay attention to conflicting data: saying one thing verbally but body language says something else. Remember, the body speaks its mind.

Thinking: What do you "think" is going on? This "meaning" contributes to your reaction. Your beliefs, interpretations, expectations, ideas, opinions, and theories influence your perception of sensory data. Thoughts are influenced by your past, present, and anticipated experiences. Your beliefs set the parameters for what you think is possible, how you feel, and what you want. Your interpretations represent how you put the world together. And your expectations are how you organize the future. Perhaps the doctor expected that the hygienist would say "No way!" and therefore made his request in a less than positive way. His beliefs and expectations sabotaged his attempt to communicate.

Tips to consider:
1. Treat your beliefs and interpretations as working hypotheses.
2. Consider the possibilities. Several interpretations may be possible.
3. Be aware of your beliefs and expectations as you approach a new situation.
4. Prepare to switch. Could you possibly change your belief or change your expectation?
5. Ask yourself: "How are my thoughts influencing what can happen in this situation? Are they limiting?"

Feeling: What do you feel? Feelings are your spontaneous internal, physical, and emotional responses to the comparison between what you expect and what you experience. Some people consider feelings to be risky, irrational, and dangerous. As a result, they fear their feelings, do not trust them, and/or try to ignore them. But if you study your feelings—feel without acting—you'll discover that your feelings are actually very predictable and rational. They come from somewhere, and how you act on them can have a positive or negative influence on the outcome of a situation.

Feelings are information. Your feelings—whatever they are—draw from other parts of your awareness. They are information about you at that moment, important in their own right. They do not have to be justified, denied, or avoided. They are part of "what is."

Several feelings can arise at the same time. At times, they can be a combination of positive and negative feelings. For example, it is possible to feel frustrated, disappointed, and hopeful all at the same time. Feelings cannot be controlled by ignoring them, nor can you do away with them by denying them. Sooner or later they will come up to haunt you. Rather than disregard your feelings – negative as well as positive – see them as internal clues to what's happening. They are your barometer; they take readings on your external and internal world. By acknowledging your feelings, you are taking control of your world.

Words used to describe feeling are words such as angry, happy, afraid, bored, excited, disappointed, concerned, and anxious.

Tips to consider:

1. Attend to your feelings. Ask yourself: "What am I feeling?" Put it in words.
2. Attune to your body. What do recurring physical sensations tell you?
3. Learn about your responses. How you respond to others reveals how you are feeling.
4. Change your activity to change your feelings.

Want: What do you want? Define your real intention. Wants are your desires, hopes, and wishes for you, for others, and for your relationships. As such, they reflect your core values. Wants can be tentative hopes and dreams or deep desires of the heart. They generally imply moving towards or away from something or someone. Wants are motivators. They give you a tentative direction for the future. They may be your mini plans, goals, objectives, or priorities.

Wants are important for two reasons: (1) over the long term, they demonstrate your real (not just stated) values; (2) they propel action. When you connect with what you really want, you focus your energy and release a strong force.

You can have wants for *yourself*, for *others*, and for *us*. One usually has multiple wants. In our example the dentist has several wants: to give the patient the best care (desire for self and others); to increase production (for us); and for his staff to participate at a different level (for self and others).

Tips to consider:

1. Ask yourself from time to time: "What do I really want?" This will give you increased energy.
2. Discover the wants of your team/others. This will assist you in motivating them.
3. Clarify wants (your own and others') to reduce confusion.
4. Check for hidden wants when you're feeling desperate. Are they keeping you stuck?
5. Use awareness of your intentions to help you send clearer messages, using an appropriate style of communication.

Action: What you do. How do you proceed to ensure that the request is followed through or behavior enhanced or changed? As you act, consider what you have done in the past, what you are doing now, and what you are willing to do going forward. Actions are behaviors, activities, action plans, solutions, promises, achievements, and accomplishments.

Tips to consider:

1. Be honest in talking about what you have done in the past and what you are willing to do differently.
2. Be realistic.

To successfully use the Awareness Wheel in your practice, get your whole team involved and learn these new communication skills together. In practicing these skills, they will be available to you when you most need them. The following example and blank Awareness Wheel will help you get your practice communication on track.

The Awareness Wheel

Start by examining each of the five zones over five weekly staff meetings. Distribute copies of the Awareness Wheel and ask each staff member to fill in each zone as you work through them.

Week One, start with the observing zone and practice reporting just what you see and hear. Pretend you are a video camera and report only the details as you see them. Using a typical office event as an example, ask staff members to look at the situation, write down what they observe, and "report" it to the rest of the team. Leave feelings and interpretations aside.

Week Two, focus on the thinking zone. Have each team member use what she learned in the first week and tell the observing portion of something she observed and expand it by adding a story to go with it (what does she think is happening or happened). Let each team member make up and share her own story. Note differences of interpretation.

Examine feelings in Week Three. Using a flip chart or dry erase board, write down all the possible feelings one can experience in a given workday. Using the example scenario, note what feelings may

The Awareness Wheel

© Copyright Sherod Miller, Daniel Wackman,
Elam Nunnally and Phyllis Miller. Used with permission.

be stirred by the interaction.

In Week Four, examine what you want from a situation. Listening to yourself and to others is very important here. When listening to others, remember you will have your turn to respond. Listen for what they really want/wanted from the situation. Give and take feedback.

In Week Five, you decide what you will do. After examining various options tied to the desired outcome, put your plan in action.

For this tool to be effective, it must be built like any habit. It will take time and commitment to make the Awareness Wheel a routine pattern of communicating. As a team, be patient with each other, ask questions for clarification, and listen carefully as you work through the Awareness Wheel. If a situation seems untenable, take time out to literally walk through the five zones, using a blank Awareness Wheel for a guide. Through this process, you and your team will be able to resolve a miscommunication.

To return to the situation at the beginning of this chapter, imagine this conversation instead.

Doctor to Hygienist:

(Observe) We have great technology here and I notice it's not being used regularly. Patients leave the office without seeing pictures of their teeth. (Think) I believe you have great talent and I believe that you want the best for your patients and the office. I think you are probably stretched for time. (Feel) I am grateful for the care you currently give the patients. I feel frustrated, however, that we are having this conversation again. I have invested in this technology that is going unused, and I get upset when I see patients leaving without the pictures. (Want) What I want is to have every patient have pictures of their teeth and for you to discuss the pictures with them. I know patients have a choice in their care and I want to be known in the community as a technologically advanced dentist. (Do) I am willing to explore options with you on how to make this work.

Hygienist to Doctor:

(Observe) When I am with a patient, I notice a change in your tone of voice and the way you look at me when you ask me about the patient. (Think) I think that you don't have any confidence in me and that you think I waste time when the patient is in my chair. I also think my pictures aren't great and I need time for training, but I don't have time to take good pictures, never mind train to take good pictures. (Feel) I feel sad, mad, and frustrated when that happens and sometimes I fear losing my job. (Want) What I want is the same as you: to be the best, for the patient to get the best, and for the team to win in that relationship. I also want to be better trained on the camera. I want to feel comfortable taking the photos. (Do) I will explore how an assistant could help me, and I will look at my schedule to set aside time for training.

Imagine having that type of conversation in your practice! The power of the Awareness Wheel cannot be underestimated. By first communicating clearly with yourself, you can walk the Awareness Wheel and know what you truly want from a conversation with someone and be more truthful not only with yourself, but with the other person. A quality conversation will occur, and you will have the satisfaction of understanding others and being understood by them.

ABOUT SHARI TASTAD, RDH, B.S.

Shari Tastad, president of Pathways, has implemented her results-oriented approach in hundreds of practices nationwide. From her extensive clinical experience, combined with ten years of coaching and consulting, Shari has developed innovative programs and business systems that maximize investment and all-around performance. She is also a professional speaker and has presented nationally on topics ranging from leadership, bottom-line business solutions, teamwork, communications, and life balance. Shari's clients have praised her as "an awesome facilitator" who helps dentists and their teams design business and life plans and then coaches them through goal realization. In addition to providing stability and a structure for success, Shari is also skilled in reuniting clients with their passions: "Not only have I realized my personal goals and exceeded my financial goals, I've never had this much fun doing dentistry!" Shari is a graduate of the University of Washington and has participated in the Integrative Program in Business Administration through their prestigious graduate school. She is a member of the Washington State Dental Hygiene Association, American Dental Hygiene Association, and the Academy of Dental Management Consultants.

Contact Information:
Shari Tastad, RDH, B.S.
Pathways, LLC
3879 10th Street SE
East Wenatchee, WA 98802
Phone: (509) 750-6603
Fax: (509) 884-8412
Email: Shari@pathwayscoaching.net
Website: www.pathwayscoaching.net

Building a Winning Team

by Tim Twigg

No management function is more critical than the ability to hire, train, motivate, and effectively manage qualified and competent people, although dental schools typically don't prepare dentists for personnel or employment law issues, and, as a result, many dentists discover that one of their primary roles is that of personnel manager. By learning the skills to turn a group of individuals into a cohesive and synergistic team, you greatly enhance your level of financial success and significantly lower your employee-related stress.

Good hiring practices and effective people skills have many common benefits. The most significant is a decrease in staff turnover and labor-related problems. The average staff member stays in an office for only about 21 months, at which time s/he will go to work for another office or leave the profession entirely. Conservative estimates are that it costs between $10,000 and $20,000 each time a turnover occurs. This cost is a combination of both indirect and direct expenses, such as recruiting through placing ads, taking time to interview, training, salaries, and lost productivity. Imagine turning that cost into profit for your practice. In an effort to do so, many practitioners are learning how to improve their hiring practices, their management skills, and their commitment to building a winning team.

One of the most common hiring mistakes inexperienced dentists make is focusing on an applicant's skills and experience, rather than his/her attitude and compatibility within the practice. Skills can be taught and experience, unfortunately, does not equate to proficiency, but attitude cannot be taught and compatibility is either there or not. Therefore, when hiring, focus first on attitude and compatibility, and then on skills and experience.

Another common hiring mistake is relying primarily on a résumé and an interview to make hiring decisions, rather than taking advantage of multiple modes of evaluation. Why use multiple modes of evaluation and selection? Statistically, when you use résumés, coupled with interviews and reference checking, your likelihood of a successful hire is only about 28 percent. When résumés, interviews, and reference checking are combined with aptitude, personality, and job matching testing, your hiring success rate will increase to 75 percent.

The process of building a winning team begins with up-to-date job descriptions. Think of job descriptions as "blueprints for hiring success." Aside from keeping you in compliance with the Americans with Disabilities Act (ADA) and state and federal laws, job descriptions are one of the best ways to establish expectations, delineate responsibilities, and create objective criteria for employee performance evaluations.

With job descriptions firmly in place, you can more confidently move to the recruiting process. Look to some of the following resources for quality applicants:

- Current employee referrals
- Patients
- Suppliers/vendors
- Schools
- Employment agencies
- Professional associations
- State Employment Department
- Newspaper advertisement
- Internet job placement services
- Community networking

While your success is somewhat dependent on the labor pool within your job market, be creative, think outside the box, and use multiple sources. Limiting yourself to just classified ads, for example, will get some response but the applicants may not be the best. Your best applicant might be your patient's son, daughter, or next door neighbor.

Typically, applicants for a job submit a résumé. While résumés may provide information regarding an applicant's previous experience and background, studies show they can also be inaccurate:

- 45 percent of résumés contain false or exaggerated information
- 53 percent falsify length of employment
- 52 percent of applicants exaggerate their experience
- 53 percent misrepresent their education or job titles

In light of these statistics, you should have all candidates complete an application. Candidates may include a résumé as supplemental information, but it should not be in lieu of completing an application.

Excellent recruiting methods will give you multiple applicants to choose from; thus you will want to conduct a pre-screening of the applicants. The primary goal is to briefly and quickly qualify or disqualify applicants. It is important to remember that well-qualified applicants will likely be exploring different practice opportunities, so it is crucial that you don't procrastinate or you risk losing a good candidate.

Develop qualifying questions that you will ask each candidate. The questions must be job-related but can range from work experience to behavioral situations, such as "describe how you would respond to a difficult patient." Typically, pre-screening occurs over the phone. If the answers are unsatisfactory, then you have no obligation to move further with that applicant. For those applicants with whom you are impressed, invite them to come in for an interview. The purpose of the structured interview is to build upon the information you already have. Effective interviewing and getting all the information you need, within legal boundaries, is both a skill and an art.

To prepare for the interview, review the information you already have on the applicant beforehand, and develop a set of specific questions to ask. Planned questions allow you to target and/or seek specific information to support a sound hiring decision, as well as avoid questions that you are not legally permitted to ask. Avoid asking questions that will elicit a "yes" or "no" answer, and focus instead on behavioral-based questions, which will elicit a more valuable and comprehensive response.

Conduct the interview in a place where you can have privacy and no interruptions. Create a relaxed, stress-free atmosphere where both you and the applicant feel comfortable. As an interviewer, your primary job is to ask questions, to listen, and to observe. A good rule to follow is that the applicant should talk about 70-80 percent of the time. Most interviewers are ineffective because they talk too much. Make notes during and after the interview. It's imperative to keep the notes focused on technical skills or experience, rather than potentially discriminatory issues. Close the interview by providing a brief overview of pertinent practice information and your philosophy. Inform the applicant of the next step in the process, but refrain from making any employment commitments.

As you narrow the candidates to two to three finalists, you will want each to take an applicant personality and aptitude test. This is a valuable aid in the selection process and is essential to getting your hiring success rate up to 75 percent. The results are designed to reveal talents, attributes, or problems that otherwise would go undetected. As a hiring tool, testing should not be the sole basis for a particular applicant's being rejected or selected. Instead, use the tool to assess perceived attributes, character strengths, and limitations relevant to the job in question. Care must be taken that the test does not discriminate, profile, or otherwise target certain groups or protected classes of prospective employees. Therefore, use only validated and approved tests, such as "Integrated Performance Management" from Bent Ericksen & Associates, which is dental profession-specific.

For those positions where evaluating specific job skills is important, you will want the remaining finalists to come in for a skills assessment. A skills assessment, different from the working interview, does not carry the same workers' compensation and unemployment risks found with the typical working interview. The basic parameters of a skills assessment include limited time (1-2 hours), not replacing a regular worker, not performing productive work, and a form confirming the voluntary/non-paid nature of the assessment, which is signed by the applicant.

As you move towards your final selection, it is important to check references and, when appropriate, to perform background checks and drug tests. These checks help reduce the potential problems associated with embezzlement, performance problems, drug or alcohol abuse, workers' compensation, claims, previous lawsuits, occupational licensing, negligent hiring and wrongful discharge claims, discrimination, and/or other claims brought by employees who are not hired or who are terminated when found unsuitable for the position. Often, just the knowledge that a reference check, background check, and/or drug test may be performed discourages applicants with a questionable background from applying.

Unfortunately, many former employers don't reveal important

information about previous or current employees. Nevertheless, you should always make a good faith effort to avoid claims of negligent hiring. Your efforts will be enhanced by asking the applicant to sign a form that permits prior employers to provide information related to the person's work performance and waives legal action related to the disclosure of such information. For consistency, the form also provides a specific routine to follow and an established set of questions to ask.

In the hiring process, background checks are becoming more and more important. Background checks can include criminal reports, driving records, social security trace/verification, credit reports, education and professional license verification, workers' compensation inquiries and/or drug testing. Workers' compensation inquiries (which are not allowed in many states) and/or drug tests can only be performed after a "conditional offer of employment" has been extended and only with the applicant's signed permission. The conditional offer essentially means that you have committed to hiring the person pending satisfactory completion of the workers' compensation inquiries and/or drug test. Relative to consumer or credit report, make sure that the information regarding someone's personal finances is relevant to the job.

By employing the selection process outlined above, you can, over a period of time, assemble the members of a winning team. That is the time to transform the members into a cohesive unit—a team, focused on your goals, including excellent service and financial success. For this transformation to occur, you must be committed to your team's success. This commitment means providing the tools, resources, training, support, and ongoing communication that will help them succeed. Too often, dentists, wanting to save a few bucks, resist investing in continuing education that would otherwise improve staff knowledge and skill. The result is lower job performance, dissatisfaction, and higher staff turnover. Compared to the costs of turnover, the cost for the continuing education would have been a bargain.

A fundamental part of managing and retaining quality staff is creating an environment, a culture if you will, that supports and acknowledges staff's contribution, individually and collectively. To create this environment, it is important to first understand what quality staff wants. Surveys show that the following 12 elements are what they want. These 12 essentials contribute to greater employee satisfaction and productivity.

Essentials for Building a Winning Team

1. Ethically sound business principles and quality patient services.
2. A consistent management style where policies are friendly, frank, fair and firm, and consistently applied and clearly explained in writing.
3. A pleasant and harmonious work environment with minimal stress.
4. Adequate facility, instruments, tools, equipment, and supplies.
5. Competent, supportive, and compatible team members.
6. Assistance in learning: to become more skilled, develop communication skills, make decisions, and take initiative.
7. Clearly defined job responsibilities and expectations.
8. Recognition as an individual and as a team member.
9. Knowledge that their efforts are being appreciated and that inadequate work performance will not be tolerated.
10. Adequate compensation and benefits.
11. Evaluation and feedback by the employer.
12. Worthwhile staff meetings.

The most effective way to support these essentials is through a comprehensive personnel policy manual. A big benefit of a good personnel policy manual is fewer staff misunderstandings, which, in turn, reduce turnover and employee-related stress.

Retaining quality staff also involves remembering that the employment relationship is a two-way street. Not just one where the employee works for you, but one where you work with the employee. Good, sound leadership is an absolute necessity for the productive growth of a business. As an employer, you inspire others through your leadership. Effective leadership means being committed to your staff and team's success. Interestingly, while many dentists say they are committed to their team's success, the statistics say otherwise. A survey of staff found that 77 percent of employees said they consider performance reviews valuable. At the same time, 33 percent indicated that they did not feel they were given feedback on their work performance.

As a leader, answer the following questions:

- Do I give my employees an opportunity to be proud of their work?
- Do I delegate all the authority I possibly can?
- Do I give them the recognition they deserve?
- Do the responsibilities of the job adequately challenge their talents and ambitions?
- Do I make the job and place of employment as pleasant and stress-free as possible?
- Do I contribute to the possibility of a promising future?

If your attitude and actions are such that you answer "yes," then you increase your odds that quality people will be attracted to your practice, will stay with you, and will want to help your practice prosper.

An essential key for supporting good communication is performance reviews. Performance reviews are critical. Evaluating job performance, providing employees with constructive feedback, and jointly discussing and addressing areas for improvement are essential for a staff person's success—remember that team success comes from the collective successes of the individuals.

Given their importance, why aren't performance evaluations done? The excuses we hear include no time, don't understand how, fear of conflict, and fear of employee reaction. Handled correctly, performance reviews can be a positive dialogue between the employer and the employee—a dialogue that focuses on ideas and solutions for improvement, using the job description's duties, responsibilities, and expectations as your objective guide. A constructive evaluation provides the staff member the opportunity to remedy performance that is less than adequate.

To the question, "When should I evaluate performance?" The short answer is "all of the time." Nothing you include in a formal performance review should come as a surprise. Don't wait until the review to share compliments and constructive criticism; use ongoing opportunities to advise employees of their progress. Know that by providing positive feedback throughout the year you will inspire better performance. As a general rule, positive feedback can be given in front of others, but negative feedback should be given in private.

New employees should receive two performance evaluations in the first 90 days: one after four weeks and a second after 11 weeks. This approach compels you to observe the new employee's performance closely. For legal and managerial reasons, it's better to let someone go during the orientation and training period rather than later.

Throughout the year, keep notes related to each employee's performance. This practice will enable you to prepare a comprehensive evaluation consisting of compliments, feedback, and a more accurate analysis of the employee. When appropriate, also relate evaluation comments to comments made in evaluations from prior years.

For consistency and ease of preparation, use specific performance evaluation forms covering items such as quality and quantity of work, job knowledge, and staff and patient relations. Resist the temptation to give everyone high marks. Be fair and honest in your analysis. Again, the evaluation should not come as a surprise to the employee if you have been communicating with him/her on an ongoing basis.

One last performance review principle to consider is separating pay raises and performance reviews. Often, when they are linked, the focus is on the money, and not on the review and ideas for improvement. When administered as separate events, have one (the review or pay adjustment) be associated with the employee's employment anniversary and the other on a calendar year basis.

As noted earlier, a fundamental part of retaining quality staff is supporting and acknowledging staff's contribution, individually and collectively. Compliments and performance appraisals are easy ways to individually support and acknowledge staff. The best way to collectively acknowledge and reward staff is through a bonus and incentive program.

Bonus plans are not about people not doing their jobs, but rather about people, working together and accomplishing more, sharing in the growth and financial success of the practice.

A good incentive program contains certain essential elements:
1. The plan needs to enlist and include all staff to stimulate and foster teamwork, business awareness, and a sense that by working together everyone will achieve more.
2. The plan needs to be easy to use, understand, and administer.
3. The plan needs to protect the practice's cash flow and overhead. In other words, no bonus is provided without the money to pay for it and cover expenses.
4. The plan, as bonuses are achieved, should drive increased profits.

A good bonus and incentive plan removes the arbitrariness of raises and allows staff to know exactly what it takes to make more money. A goal with any bonus plan is to help staff think and work more like entrepreneurs, understanding that there is more money to take home only if there is more money in the pot. Besides providing psychic ownership for the staff, a good bonus incentive plan allows you to enjoy freedom from worry, as well as the benefits of reduced negative attitudes and behaviors, management uncertainty, and salary indecisions—all of which erode productivity and consume time and energy.

Successful bonus plans are built around comparing the practice's level of business to staff costs. The level of business is technically the collections (known as revenue or gross income), but to promote team cohesiveness the practice can include production as well as collections. A simple way to relate the two is to average them together. Rather than just average each month, average two to six months together to alleviate seasonal ups and downs.

By incorporating staff-related expenses, staff is encouraged to participate in the success of the bonus plan and the overall success of the team. If the actual staff expense, on a percentage basis, exceeds the established acceptable percentage, then a bonus is not paid, and will not be paid until the percentage is back within acceptable limits. Thus the practice can realize growth (higher production and collections) and be able to pay bonuses while at the same time protecting overhead and increasing profits.

ABOUT TIM TWIGG

*A*s the owner and President of Bent Ericksen & Associates and CRC, Inc., Tim brings over 30 years of practice management and business consulting experience and knowledge specifically in the health-care field. Bent Ericksen & Associates has been the leading authority in human resources and personnel management, helping dentists success-fully deal with the ever-changing and complex labor laws. Mr. Twigg is published in many of the major healthcare journals, and he currently co-authors a monthly column in Dental Economics entitled: "Focus on Human Resources." Tim has presented seminars nationally on Personnel Management, Human Resources, and Employment Law Compliance. His expertise extends to leadership and business development, strategic marketing, and communication skills, with an emphasis on employ-ment law compliance. Presentations have included the Academy of General Dentistry Chapters, Seattle Study Club, American Association of Orthodontists, Minnesota and Florida State Dental Associations, Georgia School of Dentistry Alumni Study Club, and the Newport Harbor Academy of Dentistry. Tim is a member of the Academy of Dental Management Consultants (ADMC), the Society for Human Resource Management (SHRM), and the National Speakers Association (NSA).

Contact Information:
Tim Twigg
Bent Ericksen & Associates
P.O. Box 10542
Eugene, OR 97440
Phone: (800) 679-2760 or (541) 685-9003
Fax: (541) 685-0059
Email: info@bentericksen.com
Website: www.bentericksen.com

How to Attract, Interview, Hire & Train the Right Person for the Job

by Julie Weir

Attracting and hiring the right person for the job is every doctor's challenge. When the time comes to hire a new team member, it can often feel like the luck of the draw to end up with a motivated person who has the right behavior traits and work-style to be successful in the position. How many times have you hired a new employee and within a month found out he/she was completely different from the type of person you thought you had hired and did not really possess the behavior traits and strengths you needed? When this happens, you have invested a great deal of time and resources in the wrong person. In addition, you find yourself back on square one, starting the process of advertising, interviewing, and training a new employee all over again!

Repeating this process is very time consuming and costly. Research has shown that replacing an employee costs a business a minimum of 1.5 times the employee's annual salary. These costs include the lost productivity due to the absence of the employee and the lost productivity of the doctor and other team members who are involved in the interviewing and training process of the employee's replacement. If a doctor has two employees turn over in a year these costs could be between $75,000 to $180,000 to the practice, not to mention the stress of repeating this process on top of an already busy work schedule.

How can you break this costly cycle and find and hire the right person for your team the very first try? Below is an outline of a successful, proven, step-by-step, process for attracting, interviewing, and hiring the best person for the job. These steps will be explained in greater detail throughout the chapter.

Steps to Hiring the Right Person

1. Understand and recognize that all people possess four different behavior traits, of which one will clearly be their strongest. People also have one of three different work-style approaches. Understanding how these behavior traits and work-style approaches relate to the position you are trying to fill is the first step.
2. Create a job model of the ideal behavior traits and work-style approach that an applicant must possess to be successful in the specific job.
3. Write an effective employment advertisement to attract applicants with the qualities you desire by including specific motivators to the job model traits.
4. Survey applicants to find out their strengths, traits, and work-style approach to see how closely they match the job model so you can select the applicant with the traits you require.
5. Interview the applicants using the step-by-step process described in this chapter.

Behavior Traits

The most important point to realize when you are hiring a new employee is that people possess a mix of four different behavior traits as well as a preferred work-style approach. Professional Dynametric Programs (PDP), a worldwide leader in behavioral assessment solutions for businesses, has conducted extensive research resulting in four behavior traits defined as Dominance, Extroversion, Pace and Conformity. One of these traits will be a person's strongest and most natural way of acting and will dictate 50-70 percent of his or her behavior. PDP has defined behavior as a person's natural reactions, strengths, work-style approach, communication style, motivators/demotivators, and much more. The strengths and natural reactions of each trait are very different. It is almost as though people come from four different "planets," each with its own natural way of behaving and communicating that makes complete sense to others from the same place, but confuses those from a different planet.

A list of behaviors for each of the four traits will help you understand just how different they are.

Dominance
- Can take charge
- Comfortable with risks
- Interested in accomplishing goals and bottom-line results
- Prefer not to be bothered with details
- Can perform well with minimal controls and supervision
- Will be stressed and not stay in a work environment where they are micro managed
- Short, to-the-point communication style is often interpreted as blunt
- Can become dictatorial when stressed

Extrovert
- Outgoing, enthusiastic, motivating
- Prefers to interact with people, good with small talk and making others feel welcome and comfortable
- Thrives on positive interactions with others, praise, recognition and being part of a team
- Can be easily distracted from their work because of talking to others
- Will not stay in a work environment where they are isolated, rejected, or unappreciated
- Persuasive, talkative communication style
- Can verbally attack a coworker when stressed

Pace
- Prefers routines and working on one thing at a time
- Thrives in a stable, cooperative, harmonious work environment
- Does not adapt easily to sudden changes, needs time to think and to adjust if change occurs
- Will be stressed and/or perform poorly in an unpredictable work environment
- Warm, friendly communication style and careful to avoid confrontation
- Avoids confrontation, but, may think or act out passive aggressive actions when stressed

Conformity

- Prefers a structured work environment with standard operating procedures
- Concerned with quality, accuracy, and time to pay attention to the details
- Avoids risks and trying new things
- Seeks regular praise and confirmation of job performance, dislikes unjustified criticism
- Will be stressed and/or perform poorly in a chaotic and disorganized work environment
- Guarded, cautious, and exacting communication style
- Bury challengers with facts, inflexible, must be right when stressed

Work-Style Approach

People take three major approaches to getting a job done. Many times doctors do not understand why their employees always wait to be told what to do--why they don't just see the jobs at hand and do them. The answers lie in understanding the three work-style approaches as defined by PDP: Thrust, Ste-Nacity, and Allegiance.

Thrust

- An inner drive to push quickly to get the job done
- Initiates and completes a project or task
- Comfortable with not having an exact plan laid out before beginning a project, can figure it out along the way

Ste-Nacity

- A word coined by PDP from steadfast and tenacious
- An inner drive that gets the job done in a steady, persistent manner
- Initiates and completes a project or task

Allegiance

- Looks to an outer-directed source (doctor/supervisor) to be told what needs to be done

- Supports completing a project or task
- Hesitant to initiate project or task because of aversion to risks and mistakes

It can be very frustrating for a doctor who has a Thrust approach to interact with an employee who has the opposite style of Allegiance because it is natural for the doctor to jump in and get a project done, and he/she expects the same behavior from others. Now doctors can understand why some employees do not initiate completing projects or tasks: it is because their work-style is Allegiance and they are waiting to be told what to do. Once a doctor and employee have a better understanding of each other's work-styles, the doctor can be more proactive in directing employee actions, and the employee can be aware of the necessity to function outside of her natural comfort zones by initiating tasks. It is important when hiring new employees to know what their work-style approaches are and to decide if they match what the job will require of them. This process will also enable the doctor to manage the employee more successfully so expectations can be met.

Choosing the Right "Planet" for your Team

As you can see, the four traits and the three work-style approaches are very different from each other. Stress occurs in dental teams because doctors and team members do not understand these differences and struggle with thinking "Why can't they be more like me in the way they work?" Instead of fighting these differences, the savvy team members understand what "planet" they each come from and work with their differences to maximize the team outcome. When it comes time to hire a new team member, you want the new employee to come from the "planet" of strengths needed to perform the job and to create a good mix of diversified strengths on the team.

The applicant may have a professional appearance, decent work experience, and good references, but past work environments may have required a very different intensity of behavior traits from what your office needs. When a doctor does not assess applicants' natural behavior traits to see if they are suited for the job, he or she is missing half of the pertinent information that could be used in deciding who is the best candidate for the job. Failure to survey an applicant for behavior traits is often why the wrong people are hired, time is wasted, and productivity dollars are lost.

Road Map to a Successful New Employee

By understanding the behavior trait differences and applying these principles and techniques, a doctor's success rate in hiring the right person the first time goes up exponentially. If doctors do not survey for behavior traits, many times the hiring experience ends up like trying to put a round peg into a square hole. The doctor thought the applicant had the right traits to perform well, and the doctor and staff keep on hoping and trying to make the person work out for the job, investing good money after bad rather than understanding that the round peg will never be square.

Now there is a practical, fast, business-driven tool that provides measurable results that are designed to help the doctor create an ideal "Job Model" of desired strengths as well as survey applicants' behavior traits. Professional DynaMetric Systems (PDP) has simple, five-minute surveys that will create Job Models, help you to identify an applicant's strongest behavior traits, then analyze if his/her traits match the strengths of the Job Model—no more guessing if the applicant will really be able to perform successfully!

The following steps further explain the information thus far discussed and serve as the roadmap for hiring the right person the first time. Over the years it has been my experience that each step in this hiring process is very important and no shortcuts are effective. I have seen many doctors fail in hiring because they have tried to take short cuts and have skipped some of these steps. The results are added stress and lost time. Think of these steps as the bible to your hiring process. If you follow them closely, they will show you the truth and set you free!

1. Produce a written job description

Create or update the job description for the open position. This can be done by the doctor or a staff member and then reviewed by the doctor. This should be a clear and up-to-date job description to use as an important tool to show the applicant what you expect.

2. Create a Job Model*

Complete a PDP JobScan Survey to accurately identify the specific traits/strengths needed to perform effectively in the position you are hiring for. This survey will produce a Job Model report that can be used to match applicants against these traits. This is different from the written job description.

The use of the PDP Job Model and Applicant Surveys is highly recommended. If not using the PDP program, in another way, identify the traits and strengths you are looking for, and assess applicant strengths and traits during the interview process.

3. Write an effective classified advertisement

Realize that the best workers are often already working for someone else, but may not be satisfied.

Instead of placing the standard ad that is worded like everyone else's, write an ad that will be more effective in attracting the type of person you desire. The Job Model report will give you a list of key words/phrases that are specific motivators to the type of person you are looking for. When these motivators are written into the ad, it will prompt these good workers who are working elsewhere to call you.

4. Request applicants fax their resumes to your office

This step indicates their ability to follow directions and allows you to prescreen applicants.

5. Narrow your list of applicants through probing telephone interviews

Applicants may look good on paper but have poor interpersonal skills and substandard grammar. By speaking with applicants over the phone, you can begin to assess their skills to see if they may be a good match.

To assist doctors I have created a Telephone Screening Form; here is a sampling of questions to ask when conducting a telephone interview.

- What attracted you to this job?
- Is the practice location geographically close to you?
- What are your wage and benefit requirements?

- What days and hours are you available?
- What skills and work experience qualify you for this position?

6. Conduct a screening interview with your top candidates

I call this the "look see" interview. When the applicant arrives in the office, his or her appearance and demeanor can quickly be assessed.

- Always have the applicant fill out a job application form; look for completeness and neatness.
- Ask applicants who do not appear to be acceptable to complete an application, speak with them briefly, thank them for their time, and tell them that you are in the process of collecting information on candidates and those that are qualified will be contacted for further interviews.
- Have the applicants that appear acceptable read the job description in order to thoroughly understand the skills you need in an employee.
- Show the applicant a copy of your practice Mission Statement and discuss what it means. This is as important as the job description because the Mission Statement will tell the applicant what the team is committed to. Ask applicants if they would be able to "live" the Mission Statement as they perform their job.
- Conduct an interview to assess skills, past work experience, goals, work ethic, and values of the applicant. It is important that you go into the interview with a list of specific questions that will give you the information you must have to evaluate the applicant. Do not make the mistake of rambling on about the practice. The applicant should do 90 percent of the talking. Once you have assessed that this applicant might be a good fit, then you can describe the practice. For doctors who would like to have a list of interviewing questions, I have created three Interviewing Guides for the different office positions, (Front Desk, Assistant and Dental Hygienist) each with questions that are specific to that job. It is helpful to email this document to the applicant to complete and email back to the office for the doctor to review before the interview. This process is much more effi-

cient for the doctor and facilitates a more powerful discussion during the interview.
- If you think the applicant is the type of person you are seeking, have him/her complete a trait profiling survey before leaving your office. I recommend the PDP Applicant Survey. Say to the person: "As part of our interviewing process, we like to have applicants take a short survey that identifies specific strengths, so we can make sure the job is a good fit for you."

7. Review applicants' survey results
- Review the behavior strengths, traits, and work-style the applicant would bring to the team. It is more important to match behavior and personality traits, which are difficult to change, over job skills, which you can train for.
- Determine which applicant(s) most closely match your Job Model.

8. Check references
- Checking references is absolutely essential because many people know how to package themselves to cover up past problems or undesirable traits. Never hire without checking references!
- Always ask permission to call for references. It is helpful to have the applicant sign an Employment Reference Check Authorization to Release Information form. Calling a current employer could cost an applicant his/her job.
- While employers might be willing to confirm only employment dates, you can usually determine their overall satisfaction with that employee by their tone of voice and other comments.
- Always speak directly with the previous doctor. Ask the following questions:
  Describe your perceptions/observations of the applicant and then ask if they are correct.
  "If you had a position open up in your ofice, would you rehire this person?"
  "Is there anything else you could share with me that would help

me in considering this applicant for a position in our office?"

9. Conduct a paid working interview and a lunch out with staff

This step will provide an indicator of the applicant's current skills, ability to work with others, ability to follow directions, speed of work, and adaptability to your unique work environment.

- Pay the applicant for the time spent in the working interview.
- Have the applicant go to lunch with the office staff. The doctor pays for this lunch but does not attend. Staff should observe the applicant's treatment of the wait staff, level of politeness/manner toward other guests, and if the applicant has the same personality outside the office as demonstrated in the presence of the doctor.
- Have the staff probe as to whether the applicant is truly interested in the job or just looking for a pay check and benefits.
- Thank the applicant for his or her interest and time spent in the office. Announce a specific date by which a hiring decision will be made.

10. Make your final selection

Ask the team's opinion about hiring the applicant. Are they comfortable with this person? Are they willing to let them into the "family"? All employees want to feel a sense of value and belonging in the place they work. No matter how qualified the applicant is, if the team is unwilling to accept the person, there will be problems in the office, and the new hire will eventually leave.

11. Be sure all of your staff and the new employee are properly certified

Make verification of the applicant's certifications a condition for hiring. It is not uncommon to find dentists using assistants who had indicated they were licensed to take X-rays or administer Nitrous Oxide, but who actually are not.

Training the New Employee

The following section deals with the equally important subject of training the new recruit. Unfortunately, many well-intended doctors fail in their leadership to help the new employee reach full potential in the practice because the new employee is thrown into the fray and left to survive alone. When the following steps are taken, there is a much greater opportunity for the new employee to successfully integrate into the team and reach full potential quickly.

1. Orientation

- Create a personnel file with all necessary information.
- Review salary and benefit package with employee.
- Have the employee read the employee policy manual and sign a statement of agreement with the office policies.
- Go over the written job description.
- Create a Training Chart that lists tasks the new employee must be proficient in. Mark the tasks off as the employee demonstrates acceptable ability. The Training Chart is a good tool that will show you and the employee what is expected and the progress being made toward becoming a fully contributing team member.
- Discuss overall function of the office and how the employee should fit in.
- Introduce the person to all staff members and clarify his/her position and job description to the staff.

2. Communicate Your Practice Culture

- Culture means the behavior, attitude and communication style that is expected each day in dealing with the patients and other team members. This culture statement should also communicate your practice philosophy and beliefs.
- Share and discuss the practice's mission statement, what it means, and how to "live it" in the office.

3. Encourage Team Relationships

- Arrange to have each of the different staff members that will be working closely with the new employee to take him or her to lunch.

4. Employee Shadows Doctor/Supervisor

- New employee is able to see how job is done well.
- Employee should be encouraged to ask questions.

5. Doctor/Supervisor Shadows Employee
- Supervisor "coaches" employee for great performance as they perform tasks.
- Employee is encouraged to ask questions.

6. Training method: Tell, Show, Do
- Tell the employee what the importance of each function is and how it fits into the "big picture."
- Ask the following questions when training:
  "What do you know about this?"
  "What are your strengths, weaknesses?"
  "How can I best teach you?"
- Tell the employee the "benchmark" of acceptable performance for each job function.
- Have the employee role play as much as possible in order to assume ownership of the new behavior/skill.

7. Doctor/Supervisor Debriefing/Coaching
The employee's immediate supervisor should give a five-to-ten minute debriefing at the end of each day to coach the employee on what was done well and what needs to be done differently, including the reasons why. This should take place every day for the first two weeks. During weeks three and four, every other day is sufficient. Finally, the supervisor should also conduct a specific 30-day review. During debriefing time:
- Tell employee what was done well that day.
- Explain what you would like done differently and how.
- Tell what you want the employee to focus on the next day.
- Ask:
  "What was your biggest struggle today?"
  "What would you like me to help you with tomorrow?"
  "What did you learn today that impacted you the most?"

Encourage the doctor(s) that are in the office that day to give the employee a quick debriefing. These debriefings are to be a positive and encouraging learning experience for the employee. Remember, you are mentoring the new employee for success.

8. How to Coach in a Positive Way

- Keep the coaching environment positive because people thrive in a positive environment versus a punitive and negative environment.
- It is important that you balance your coaching requests for the different performance with the appropriate amount of positive feedback.
- As you are coaching and giving the employee feedback on performance, always begin with what is being done well. Sincerely praise unique strengths, what has been done right, and the value the new employee brings to the team.
- Then, use the word "now" as you move into the discussion of what you would like done differently. Give reasons why the job needs to be done differently.
- Ask the employee for questions or suggestions as to what the team could do to help the employee achieve the level of performance just discussed.
- End the discussion on a positive note by expressing that you are confident that the employee will reach the desired level of performance.

As many doctors realize, their practice can only be as good as the people they hire. The levels of professionalism, clinical excellence, productivity, profitability, and job satisfaction are dictated by the sum of what the dental team members contribute. Doctors should realize the extent of the impact each employee can have on the success or failure of a practice. By taking the time and effort to hire and train the right person the first time, you will save yourself a lot of stress, frustration, and money and acquire a highly qualified and productive new member for your team.

Information about using the Professional DynaMetric Programs (PDP) to create Job Models, writing more effective employment ads, surveying applicants and many of the forms or charts that were referenced in this chapter are available at www.julieweir.com/hire.htm.

ABOUT JULIE WEIR

*J*ulie Weir is known for her dynamic, energetic, and entertaining style that captivates dental teams with practical information they can relate to. Because of her hands-on ownership experience in a dental practice, Julie brings a unique management blend of both the business and clinical aspects of dentistry into her talks. With more than 30 years of experience, she has worked as a hygienist, dental assistant, and office manager, and has held a clinical teaching position at The University of Michigan School of Dentistry. From 1982 through 1991 she was in charge of all business systems and management, with ownership responsibilities, in a practice that consistently maintained production numbers in the top 5 percent of the nation. In 1995 Julie founded her full service management consulting company and is dedicated to working closely with doctors and staff to improve their lives professionally, financially and personally by implementing proven systems and philosophies that ensure practice success. Julie received her Bachelor of Science in Dental Hygiene from The University of Michigan in 1976, and has been an active member of The Academy of Dental Management Consultants since 1997. Being a Certified DynaMetrics Professional allows her to coach doctors and staff to better select, manage, and understand individual working styles, which lead to better team interaction and productivity. Julie has been published in numerous dental journals and is the author of the book 10 Steps to a Dental Practice Business Plan. She has spoken at regional, national and international dental association conferences.*

Contact Information:
Julie Weir
Dental Practice Management, Ltd.
15520 Herring Road
Colorado Springs, CO 80908
Phone: (719) 495-8735
Email: julie@julieweir.com
Website: www.julieweir.com

Resource Listing

TIM BREIDING
Breiding Marketing
11181 Scullers Run
Tega Cay, SC 29708
Phone/Fax: (803) 548-9868
Email: timtegacay@aol.com
Website: www.breidingmarketing.com

LINDA DREVENSTEDT, M.S.
Drevenstedt Consulting LLC
1093 A1A Beach Boulevard, #378
St. Augustine, FL 32080
Phone: (800) 242-7648
Fax: (904) 794-5582
Email: linda@drevenstedt.com
Website: www.drevenstedt.com

KATHERINE EITEL
Katherine Eitel & Associates
P.O. Box 423
Aguanga, CA 92536
Phone: (800) 595-7060
Fax: (951) 693-1477
Email: info@katherineeitel.com
Website: www.katherineeitel.com

JUDY GOLDMAN
Practice Development Associates
81 Cook Court
Chula Vista, CA 91910
Phone: (619) 691-7990
Fax: (619) 691-7970
Email: practdev@aol.com
Website: www.pda-judygoldman.com

PAULINE GRABOWSKI
Pauline Grabowski & Associates
P.O. Box 15528
Chesapeake, VA 23322
Phone: (757) 497-2040
Fax: (757) 482-7047
Email: pmgmgt@aol.com
Website: www.paulinegrabowski.com

LARRY M. GUZZARDO
Larry M. Guzzardo, Inc.
P.O. Box 421635
405 Meadowbrook Drive, #100
Atlanta, GA 30342
Phone: (404) 252-5664
Fax: (404) 252-9157
Email: LMGuzzardo@aol.com

CINDY J. ISHIMOTO, CDPMA
Practice Excellence
314 Ekoa Place
Wailuku, HI 96793
Phone/Fax: (808) 244-7344
Email: CIshimoto@aol.com

CATHY JAMESON
Jameson Management Group
P.O. Box 488
Davis, OK 73030
Phone: (580) 369-5555
    or (800) 637-3947
Fax: (580) 369-3352
Email: info@jamesonmanagement.com
Website: www.jamesonmanagement.com

LINDA MILES, CSP, CMC
Linda L. Miles & Associates
P.O. Box 6249
Virginia Beach, VA 23456
Phone: (757) 721-3332
    or (800) 922-0866
Fax: (757) 721-2892
Email: LLMiles@is.netcom.com
Website: www.DentalManagementU.com

RHONDA MULLINS
VistaPro Consulting, Inc.
400 East Point Drive
Canton, GA 30115
Phone: (770) 720-1766
Fax: (770) 720-9895
Email: rhonda@rhondamullins.com
Website: www.rhondamullins.com

LISA PHILP, RDH, CMC
Transitions Group North America
3050 Harvester Road, #205
Burlington, Ontario, Canada L7N3J1
Phone: (905) 681-1011
Fax: (905) 681-1180
Email: lphilp@tcgdds.com

SHARI TASTAD, RDH, B.S.
Pathways, LLC
3879 10th Street SE
East Wenatchee, WA 98802
Phone: (509) 750-6603
Fax: (509) 884-8412
Email: shari@pathwayscoaching.net
Website: www.pathwayscoaching.net

TIM TWIGG
Bent Ericksen & Associates
P.O. Box 10542
Eugene, OR 97440
Phone: (541) 685-9003
Fax: (541) 685-0059
Email: timtwigg@msn.com

JULIE WEIR
Weir Dental Practice Management
15520 Herring Road
Colorado Springs, CO 80908
Phone: (719) 495-8735
Fax: (719) 495-0422
Email: WDental@aol.com
Website: www.julieweir.com

Active Members & Staff
February 1, 2006

ANDERSON, LINDA
Member since 7/05
Transitions Group
3030 Harvester Road, #205
Burlington, Ontario L7N3J1 Canada
Phone: (905) 681-9157
Fax: (905) 681-1180
Email: linda@tdgdds.com

BANTA, LOIS
Member since 5/01
Member at Large 02/04
Secretary 04/06
Banta Consulting Inc.
33020 NE Pink Hill Road
Grain Valley, MO 64029
Phone: (816) 847-2055
Fax: (816) 847-5962
Email: loisbanta@kcnet.com

BREIDING, TIMOTHY
Member since 4/99
Secretary 00/02
Marketing Committee 00/02
VP/President Elect 02/04
President 04/06
Breiding Marketing
11181 Scullers Run
Tega Cay, SC 29708
Phone/Fax: (803) 548-9868
Email: timtegacay@aol.com
Website: www.breidingmarketing.com

BRYANT, BELINDA
Member since 3/95
Educational Chairman 97/98/99
Nominating Committee 98
Vice Pres/President Elect 98/00
President 00/02
Immediate Past President 02/04
Belinda Bryant Consulting
222 Doke-Cohran Road
Dallas, GA 30132
Phone: (770) 445-0821
Fax: (770) 445-8658
Email: belinda@bbryantconsulting.com

CARTER, D'JEAN
Member since 10/02
D'Jean Carter & Associates, Inc.
13 Wicklow Drive
Hilton Head Island, SC 29928
Phone: (877) 738-8314 or (843) 842-4022
Fax: (843) 842-9344
Email: djcarter@earthlink.net

CASTAGNA, DEBBIE
Member since 10/98
Sponsorship Committee 98/00
Secretary 02/04
Insight Solution
38 Creekside Court
Corte Madrea, CA 94925
Phone: (415) 924-5213
Fax: (415) 924-5970
Email: dcastagna@insight-solution.com
Website: www.insight-solution.com

CATALANELLO, JODY
Member since 8/97
Educational Committee 98/00
Member at Large 02/04
Mosaic Management Group
2009 N. Seminary
Chicago, IL 60614
Phone: (773) 525-6488
Fax: (773) 525-6463
Email: Jody@mosaicmanagementgroup.com

CHRISTENSEN, GAYLE
Member since 10/03
Management Resoures, LLC
13640 Alamo Street, NE
Ham Lake, MN 55304
Phone: (763) 755-4087
Fax: (763) 862-6410
Email: gayle_christensen@msn.com

COOPER, PEGGY
Member since 9/02
Cooper & Company, Inc.
P.O. Box 15907
Augusta, GA 30919
Phone: (706) 737-0373
Fax: (706) 737-0199
Email: peggy@cooperandco.com

DEMAREE, HAROLD
Member since 10/98
Educational Committee 98/00
T.H.E. Design, Inc.
901 S. Mopac Expressway
Building 2, Suite 420
Austin, TX 78746
Phone: (512) 328-7744
Fax: (512) 328-7474
Email: harry@thedesign.com

DiGIAMBATTISTA, SUSAN
Executive Director
Trojan Professional Services
P.O. Box 1270
Los Alamitos, CA 90720
Phone: (800) 451-9723
Fax: (800) 282-6345
Email: susand@trojanonline.com

DREVENSTEDT, LINDA
Member at Large 98/00, 00/02
Member since 10/97
Marketing Committee 98/00, 00/02
Marketing Committee 98/00, 00/02
Marketing Committee 04/06
Drevenstedt Consulting LLC
1093 A1A Beach Boulevard, #378
St. Augustine, FL 32080
Phone: (800) 242-7648
Fax: (904) 794-5582
Email: linda@drevenstedt.com
Website: www.drevenstedt.com

EITEL, KATHERINE
Member since 5/96
Nominating Committee 96/98
Secretary 98/00
Educational Committee 98/00
Membership Committee 00/02
VP/President Elect 04/06
Katherine Eitel & Associates
P.O. Box 423
Aguanga, CA 92536
Phone: (800) 595-7060
Fax: (951) 693-1477
Email: info@katherineeitel.com
Website: www.katherineeitel.com

ENGELHARDT-NASH, DEBRA *Founding*
Member 1987
Immediate Past President 94/96
President 93/94
Newsletter Committee 93/94
Sponsorship Committee 93/94
Nominating Committee 94/96
Charles Kidd Spirit Award 94
Education Chairman 96/98, 02/04
Vice President/President Elect 92
Secretary 91
Debra Engelhardt & Associates Inc.
2809 Coltsgate Road, #200
Charlotte, NC 28211
Phone: (704)442-0242 or (888) 442-0242
Fax: (704) 364-1963
New York Office:
250 Park Avenue South
New York, NY 10003
Email: rdnash@aol.com

ERICKSEN, BENT
Founding Member 1987
Ethics Committee 91/92
Membership Committee 93/94
Bent Ericksen & Associates
3941 Park Drive., #20-317
El Dorado Hills, CA 95761
Phone: (916) 933-5106
Fax: (916) 933-0973
Main Office:
P.O. Box 10542
Eugene, OR 97440
Phone: (800) 679-2160
Fax: (541) 685-0059
Email: bent@bentericksen.com

FREEMAN, MARSHA
Member since 7/93
Secretary 94/96
Secretary 96/98
Educational Committee 98/00
Newsletter Committee 98/00
Education Committee 00/02
Marsha Freeman & Associates
P.O. Box 68
Nipomo, CA 93444
Phone: (800) 253-2544 or (805) 929-0454
Fax: (805) 929-0931
Email: marsha@fix.net
Website: www.marshafreeman.com

GOLDMAN, JUDY
Member since 7/99
Practice Development Associates
81 Cook Court
Chula Vista, CA 91910
Phone: (619) 691-7990
Fax: (619) 691-7970
Email: practdev@aol.com
Website: www.pda-judygoldman.com

GOLDSTEIN, JEFFREY
Founding Member 1987
Returning Member 4/99
Membership Committee 02/04
Barron & Goldstein
2239 Cheremoya Avenue
Los Angeles, CA 90068
Phone: (323) 463-2444
FAX (323) 463-8108
Email: jgoldst@ucla.edu

GORRELL, PAMELA A.
Members since 12/97
Nominating Committee 98/00
Mosaic Management Group
2051 Madelaine Court
Los Altos, CA 94024
Phone: (650) 968-2809
Fax: (650) 968-6209
Email: pamosaic@ix.netcom.com

GOVONI, MARY
Member since 1/02
Clinical Dynamics
2435 Seville Drive
Okemos, MI 48864
Phone: (517) 347-7903
Fax: (517) 349-6356
Email: govonim@aol.com

GRABOWSKI, PAULINE
Member since 1/03
Pauline Grabowski & Associates
P.O. Box 15528
Chesapeake, VA 23322
Phone: (757) 497-2040
Fax: (757) 482-7047
Email: pmgmgt@aol.com
Website: www.paulinegrabowski.com

GRANTHAM, LAUREL
Member since 8/04
Grantham Consulting Solutions, Inc.
1 Kentwood Drive
Smithfield, NC 27577
Phone: (919) 934-1549
Fax: (919) 934-0300
Email: lagrantham@yahoo.com

GUNN, SUSAN
Member since 10/03
Gunn Consulting
P.O. Box 13806
Arlington, TX 76094
Phone: (817) 994-3167
Fax: (817) 275-2012
Email: s.gunn@gunnconsulting.com

GUZZARDO, LARRY
Member since 12/97
Membership Committee 00/02
Larry M. Guzzardo, Inc.
P.O. Box 421635
405 Meadowbrook Drive, #100
Atlanta, GA 30342
Phone: (404) 252-5664
Fax: (404) 252-9157
Email: LMGuzzardo@aol.com

HANSON, DONALD G.
Affiliate Member since 7/05
Quality Transitions
1400 Wisconsin Avenue, #118
Whitefish, MT 59937
Mailing Address:
P.O. Box 4556
Whitefish, MT 59937
Phone/Fax: (406) 862-6260
Email: dghanson62@aol.com
Website: www.qualitytransitions.com

HEGARTY, GINNY
Member since 1/04
Ginny Hegarty Dental Practice
Development
1608 Barbara Drive
Downingtown, PA 19335
Phone: (610) 873-8404
Fax: (610) 873-8405
Email: ginny@ginnyhegarty.com
Website: www.ginnyhegarty.com
        www.officemagic.com

HEILMAN, REBECCA
Member since 7/99
Education Committee 00/02
Heilman & Associates
100 Osprey Ridge Way
Ponte Vedra Beach, FL 32082
Phone: (904) 273-8554
Fax: (904) 273-8830
Email: rebeccaheilmandh@bellsouth.net

HENDERSON-STEENSON, SHERRI
Member since 2/97
Marketing Committee 98/00
Education Committee 00/02
Nominating Committee 00/02
Membership Committee 02/04
Sherri L. Henderson & Associates
921 Circle in the Woods
Fairview, TX 75069
Phone: (972) 562-1072
Fax: (972) 562-0379
Email: Sherrislh@direcway.com

HERYFORD, MELINDA
Member since 7/93
Member at Large 04/06
Melinda G. Heryford & Associates
P.O. Box 660934
Sacramento, CA 95866
Phone: (916) 488-1929
Fax: (916) 488-2913
Email: Melindah@inreach.com

HOMOLY, PAUL
Member since 3/04
Homoly Communications
2101 N. Aurelius Road, #4-A
Holt, MI 48842
Phone: (517) 694-8500
Fax: (517) 694-8558
Email: paul@paulhomoly.com
Website: www.paulhomoly.com

HURLEY-TRAILOR, JANICE
Member since 1/94
Newsletter Committee 94/96
Member at Large 94/96
Member at Large 96/98
Janice Hurley & Associates
6833 E. Montreal Place
Scottsdale, AZ 85254
Phone: (480) 219-3860
Fax: (480) 219-4364
Email: jhurley@thegrid.net
Website: www.janicehurley.com

ISHIMOTO, CINDY J.
Member since 10/98
Membership Committee 98/00
Education Committee 00/02, 02/04
Practice Excellence
314 Ekoa Place
Wailuku, HI 96793
Phone/Fax: (808) 244-7344
Email: CIshimoto@aol.com

ISMAN, DEBRA
Member since 3/95
Educational Committee 98/00
Isman Consulting
2211 Norfolk Street, #613
Houston, TX 77098
Phone/Fax: (713) 522-6670
Email: debraisman@aol.com

JAMESON, CATHY
Member since 7/92
Sponsorship 94/96
Jameson Management Group
P.O. Box 488
Davis, OK 73030
Phone: (580) 369-5555 or (800) 637-3947
Fax: (580) 369-3352
Email: info@jamesonmanagement.com
Website: www.jamesonmanagement.com

JAMISON, LAURA
Member since 7/05
Jamison Consulting, Inc.
711 S. Rome Avenue
Tampa, FL 33606
Phone: (813) 251-6401
Fax: (813) 251-3351
Email: jamisonconsulting@
tampabay.rr.com

JOHNSON, KATHLEEN
Member since 6/99
Member at Large 00/02
Sponsorship Committee 02/04
Kathleen Johnson & Associates
6074 Silverspur Trail
Anaheim Hills, CA 92807
Phone: (800) 998-8399 or (714) 974-7828
Fax: (714) 974-7864
Email: kajohnson@sbcglobal.net

KENT, JANELL
Member since 8/04
Developmental Dental Strategies
(DDS Consulting)
1136 NE Pine Island Road, #15
Cape Coral, FL 33909
Phone: (239) 772-7875 or (866) 862-7875
Fax: (239) 772-1427
Email: jkent91314 @msn.com
Website: www.ddsmanagement.com

KIZER, LYNDA
Member since 10/2000
Lynda Kizer & Associates, Inc.
7585 S. Prescott Street
Littleton, CO 80120
Phone: (303) 794-6642
Fax: (303) 794-1395
Email: Lyndakizer@worldnet.att.net

KULAKOWSKI, SUSAN
Member since 8/04
Developmental Dental Strategies
(DDS Consulting)
536 Monaco Drive
Punta Gorda, FL 33950
Phone: (866) 862-7875
Fax: (209) 391-3273
Email: sueziqk @msn.com
Website: www.ddsmanagement.com

LAVINE, LORNE
Member since 10/03
Dental Technology Consultants
4540 Tobias Avenue
Sherman Oaks, CA 91403
Phone: (866) 204-3398
Fax: (818) 788-3658
Email: drlavine@thedigitaldentist.com
Website: www.thedigitaldentist.com

LAWRENCE, MELINDA
Affiliate Member since 10/04
Melinda Lawrence Consulting
4358 Preserve Place
Edmonds, OK 73034
Phone: (405) 285-8192
Email: mellokc@cox.net

LIMOLI, TOM JR.
Member since 7/93
Vice Pres/President Elect 94/96
Newsletter Committee 94/96
President 96/98
Past President 98/00
Nominating Committee 98/00
Atlanta Dental Consultants
P.O. Box 420947
Atlanta, GA 30342
Phone: (404) 252-7808 or (800) 344-2633
Fax: (404) 843-1564
Email: limolijr@bellsouth.net
Website: www.limoli.com

LOCKE , SUSAN
Member since 8/05
Coaching Solutions
606 Parry Boulevard
Cinnaminson, NJ 08077
Phone: (856) 786-4814
Fax: (856) 786-4815
Email: lockekbt@aol.com

LUCHT, STEPHEN R.
Member since 7/99
Lucht & Associates, Inc.
2142 Langston Lane, NE
St. Michael, MN 55376
Phone: (763) 497-9386
Fax: (763) 497-9387
Email: Slucht@charter.net

MAGUIRE, BEVERLY
Member since 12/99
Marketing Committee
Perio Advocates
P.O. Box 167
Fairfax Station, VA 22039
Phone: (703) 269-3125
Email: PerioAdvocates@aol.com

MILES, LINDA
Member since 1/94
Member at Large 98/00
Nominating Committee 00/02
Linda L. Miles & Associates
P.O. Box 6249
Virginia Beach, VA 23456
Phone: (757) 721-3332 or (800) 922-0866
Fax: (757) 721-2892
Email: LLMiles@is.netcom.com
Website: www.DentalManagementU.com

MOORE, VIRGINIA
Member since 11/97
Member at Large 98/00
Vice President/President Elect 00/02
President 02/04
Immediate Past President 04/06
Insight Solution
1010 Jefferson Street
Red Bluff, CA 96080
Phone: (530) 527-9457
Fax: (530) 527-1568
Email: vmoore@insight-solution.com
Website: www.insight-solution.com

MULLINS, RHONDA
Member since 1998
VistaPro Consulting, Inc.
400 East Point Drive
Canton, GA 30115
Phone: (770) 720-1766
Fax: (770) 720-9895
Email: rhonda@rhondamullins.com
Website: www.rhondamullins.com

NIELSEN, KATE
Member since 10/04
Tucci Management Consulting, Inc.
84 Larch Street
Hamilton Ontario L8T4P3 CANADA
Phone: (905) 574-0701
FAX (905) 764-7535
Email: tuccimgmtkate@hotmail.com

O'DONNELL, KATHLEEN
Member since 6/99
14 Kaly Lane
P.O. Box 70
Harpswell, ME 04079
Phone: (207) 883-7799
Fax: (207) 833-6699
Email: kmodonnell@earthlink.net

PANGAKIS, FRAN
Affiliate member since 7/05
Coaching Solutions
121 Cross Keys Road, #F
Baltimore, MD 21210
Phone: (410) 323-092 0
Fax: (410) 323-0921
Email: pangakisf@aol.com

PHILP, LISA
Member since 12/00
Membership Committee 02/04
Transitions Group
3050 Harvester Road, #205
Burlington, Ontario, Canada L7N3J1
Phone: (905) 681-1011
Fax: (905) 681-1180
Email: lphilp@tcgdds.com

PLANKERS, TAMMARA
Member since 6/00
Newsletter Committee 00/02
The Matsco Companies
2000 Powell Street, 4th Floor
Emeryville, CA 94608
Phone: (510) 450-3100 or (800) 326-0376
Fax: (510) 450-3010
Email: tammara.plankers@matsco.com

REZNIK, DAVID M.
Member since 4/98
Sponsorship Chairman 98/00, 00/02,
02/04
Member at Large 00/02
Sky's The Limit Productions, Inc.
2835 S. Clark Drive
East Point, GA 30344
Phone: (404) 762-8774
Fax: (404) 763-0317
Email: davidmreznik@yahoo.com

ROMERO, ANDRÉS M.
Member since 5/05
Dental Financial Services
1100 Circle 75 Parkway, #1500
Atlanta, GA 30339
Phone: (770) 612-6335
Fax: (770) 955-0725
Email: andresmromero@yahoo.com

SANCO, VICKI C.
Member since 3/98
Membership Committee 98/00
Marketing Committee 02/04
Jameson Management, Inc.
8311 County Road, #802A
Burleson, TX 76028
Phone: (817) 705-5623
Fax: (817) 447-4724
Email: vickis@jamesonmanagement.com

SIMON, RISA
Founding Member 1987
Membership Committee 91
Education Committee 91, 93/94
Vice President/President Elect 91
President 92
Past President 92/93
Nominating Committee 93/94
Charles Kidd Spirit Award 94
Membership Committee 94/96
Simon Says Solutions
(Division of Simon Says Seminars, Inc.)
34522 N. Scottsdale Road
Scottsdale, AZ 85262
Phone: (480) 575-9353
Fax: (480) 575-9357
Email: risa@simonsayssolutions.com
Website: www.simonsayssolutions.com

SMITH, AMY
Member since 10/04
Benco Dental Co.
46 Michael Road
Bridgewater, MA 02324
Phone: (508) 697-7318
Fax: (508) 697-7327
Email: as2smile@comcast.net or
asmith@benco.com

SPEAR, SUSAN
Member since 7/02
Marketing Committee 02/04
Member at Large 04/06
SAS Transitions
7042 S. Lewis Court
Littleton, CO 80127
Phone: (303) 973-2147
Fax: (303) 973-1710
Email: susan@sastransitions.com

STEWARD, JANET
Member since 11/04
Steward & Associates
2768 Canby Way
Fort Collins, CO 80525
Phone: (970) 207-0776 or (877) 599-0099
Fax: (970) 223-7916
Email: Janet@stewardassociates.biz
Website: www.stewardassociates.biz

STRAINE, KERRY
Member since 10/00
Straine Consulting
838 University Avenue
Sacramento, CA 95825
Phone: (800) 568-7200 or (916) 568-7200
Fax: (916) 568-7100
Email: kerry@straine.com
Website: www.straine.com

SWEENEY, CHAR
Member since 2/96
Sweeney & Associates
2425 Military Street, Building 3
Port Huron, MI 48060
Phone: (800) 987-8776
Fax: (810) 985-6675
Email: csweeneyph@aol.com

TASTAD, SHARI
Member since 3/04
Pathways, LLC
3879 10th Street SE
East Wenatchee, WA 98802
Phone: (509) 750-6603
Fax: (509) 884-8412
Email: shari@pathwayscoaching.net
Website: www.pathwayscoaching.net

TUCCI, DALE
Member since 10/95
Tucci Management Consultants
90 Bassett Avenue
Richmond Hill
Ontario, L4B4G1 CANADA
Phone: (905) 764-7518
Fax: (905) 764-7535
Email: tuccimgmt@rogers.com

TWIGG, TIMOTHY
Member since 2/03
Member at Large 04/06
Bent Ericksen & Associates
P.O. Box 10542
Eugene, OR 97440
Phone: (541) 685-9003
Fax: (541) 685-0059
Email: timtwigg@msn.com

VALENCIA, LINDA
Member since 8/97
Nominating Committee 98/00
Mosaic Management Group
4442 W. Berteau Avenue
Chicago, IL 60641
Phone: (773) 202-9832
Fax: (773) 202-9834
Email: lwvalencia@mindparing.com

WALKER, TERESA B.
Member Since 10/97
Newsletter Committee 98/00
Anderson Associates/DenCor
Management Services, Inc.
104 Gainsborough Drive
Dallas, GA 30157
Phone: (770) 505-8407
FAX (770) 505-1186
Email: Tande16434@aol.com

WAITE, PHYLLIS
Founding Member 1987
Ethics Committee 91/92
Newsletter Committee 92/94, 00/02
Education Committee 93/94
Vice President/President Elect 93/94
President 94/96
Past President 96/98
Marketing Committee 98/00
Sponsorship Committee 98/00
Charles Kidd Spirit Award 99
Phyllis Waite & Associates
19451 Riverdale Lane, #A
Huntington Beach, CA 92648
Phone: (714) 536-0603
Fax: (714) 536-5859
Email: pwadental.@aol.com

WANN, OLIVIA M.
Member since 9/02
Modern Practice Solutions
P.O. Box 252
Dover, TN 37058
Phone: (615) 308-6695
Fax: (931) 232-7738
Email: dogwood@compu.net

WEIR, JULIE
Member since 1/97
Member at Large 04/06
Weir Dental Practice Management
15520 Herring Road
Colorado Springs, CO 80908
Phone: (719) 495-8735
Fax: (719) 495-0422
Email: WDental@aol.com
Website: www.julieweir.com

WHEAT, BETSY
Member since 8/92
Education Chairman 94/96
Vice Pres/President Elect 96/98 President 98/00
Past President 00/02
Nominating Committee 00/02
Innovative Practice Management
P.O. Box 866065,
Plano, TX 75086
Phone: (972) 208-4911
Fax: (972) 208-4912
Email: wheatipm@aol.com

WILKINSON, SHURLI
Founding Member 1987
Returning Member 1998
Wilkinson Management Consulting
34522 N. Scottsdale Rd.
#200 Scottsdale, AZ 85262
Phone: (877) 274-8754
Fax: (877) 964-5214
Email: ShurliWilkinson@usa.net
Website: www.shurliwilkinson.com

WILLEFORD, RAYMOND (RICK)
Member since 3/04
Willeford Haile & Associates, CPA PC
600 Houze Way, #D-6,
Roswell, GA 30076
Phone: (770) 552-8500
Fax: (770) 552-9307
Email: rickw@willefordcpa.com
Website: www.willefordcpa.com

YEARSLEY, PEGGY
Founding Member 1987-93
Membership Committee 90/91
Newsletter Committee 90/91
Member at Large 90/91
Returning Member 9/98
Peggy Yearsley Dental Marketing
Consultant
1903 W. 8th St., #109
Erie, PA 16505
Phone: (814) 836-1635
Fax: (814) 836-7646
Email: ply@earthlink.net